THE REGULATION OF PRIVACY AND DATA PROTECTION IN THE USE OF ELECTRONIC HEALTH INFORMATION

An International Perspective and Reference Source on Regulatory and Legal Issues Related to Person-Identifiable Health Databases

R. J. Rodrigues
P. Wilson
S. J. Schanz

PAN AMERICAN HEALTH ORGANIZATION
Pan American Sanitary Bureau, Regional Office of the
WORLD HEALTH ORGANIZATION

DIVISION OF HEALTH SYSTEMS AND SERVICES DEVELOPMENT
ESSENTIAL DRUGS AND TECHNOLOGY PROGRAM

PAHO Cataloguing-in-Publication

Pan American Health Organization
The Regulation of Privacy and Data Protection in the Use of Electronic Health Information:
An International Perspective and Reference Source on Regulatory and Legal Issues Related to
Person-Identifiable Health Databases
Washington, D.C.: PAHO, © 2001. 217 p.

ISBN 92 75 12385 3

I. Title   II. Rodrigues, R.J.
III. Wilson, P.   IV. Schanz, S.J.

1. MEDICAL INFORMATICS
2. INFORMATION SYSTEMS
3. TECHNOLOGY CONTROL
4. LEGISLATION
5. DATABASES
6. REGULATION
7. NATIONAL LAWS REVISION

LC K5438.P187r 2001

ISBN 92 75 12385 3

Roberto J. Rodrigues

Regional Advisor, Health Services Information Technology
Division of Health Systems and Services Development
Pan American Health Organization / World Health Organization
Washington, D.C., USA

Petra Wilson *

Scientific Officer
European Commission, Directorate General for
Information Society Applications Relating to Health
Brussels, Belgium

Stephen J. Schanz

Adjunct Associate Professor
East Carolina University School of Medicine
Greenville, North Carolina, USA

President
Legamed, Inc.
Raleigh, North Carolina, USA

*The opinions expressed are those of the author and do not
necessarily reflect the position of the European Commission*

Note from the Authors

The study of legal issues in the field of medical informatics must not only limit itself to existing legislation which are relevant in this matter such as data protection and privacy, but must be forward looking and anticipate legal issues that, although not yet addressed in legislation or litigation, may become legal obstacles in the near future as applications of information technology become more widely used. Furthermore, legal research must take into account the totality and diversities of healthcare systems from and international perspective and the way in which these are organized, financed, and run.

> - Laske C (1996). *Legal issues in medical informatics: a bird's eye view.* In: Barber B, Treacher A, Louwerse K (eds). *Towards Security in Medical Informatics: Legal and Ethical Aspects.* ISO Press, Oxford

The challenges faced in the preparation of this publication were twofold; first, how to deal with the massive amount of extant regulatory and legal documents, many only available in national languages and second, chasing the moving target represented by the fast changes occurring in the areas of regulation and law. Because our chief intention was to provide a wide-ranging view of the issues related to individually identifiable health databases, many aspects may have not received the in-depth coverage that they deserve. We hope that the substantial list of references will be advantageously used by those who want to pursue more complete studies.

A very large number of online sources were consulted and they are listed in Chapter 13. We would like, however, to individually recognize the exceptional collection of information available at the *Privacy International* website. The site is maintained by a very active human rights group with broad interest in all aspects of privacy – we made extensive use of their resources and analytical summaries in the preparation of the country reports included in this publication.

We want also to acknowledge the contribution to the section on the European Community, by our colleagues José Luís Monteagudo Peña and Marcelo Sosa-ludicissa from the Instituto de Salud Carlos III, Ministerio de Sanidad y Consumo, Madrid.

Foreword

With the rapid dissemination of information and communication technologies, there has been a growing concern about the collection, processing, storage, access, and exchange of data related to individuals. The ethical and legal issues of data protection and privacy have been the focus of attention of lawmakers in many countries and there is a manifest feeling of urgency in ensuring that privacy rules apply to personal data. Privacy regulation and legislation are being set off by fears that information technology resources being used by online commerce, government agencies, insurance companies, and health providers and payers are increasingly making it easy for companies and organizations to compile sophisticated data repositories of person identifiable data. Content, access, and use of those data repositories are at the core of the many questions being raised by the civil society, health professionals, and privacy advocates.

The authors review the fundamental concepts related to the technical and legal aspects of data protection and summarize the scope and degree of implementation of pertinent regulation in fifty-one countries. Even though the emphasis of the book is on data protection and privacy issues as they relate to person identifiable electronic databases, data privacy regulation and legislation being implemented in many countries will likely apply to all data, regardless whether they are collected offline or online.

Health professionals, legislators, and other interested parties will find in this publication of the Essential Drugs and Technology Program, Division of Health Systems and Services Development, a valuable, carefully researched, and extensively referenced source of information on the present status of health data protection regulation.

George A.O. Alleyne
Director
Pan American Health Organization

TABLE OF CONTENTS

1. **INFORMATION AND COMMUNICATION TECHNOLOGIES IN HEALTHCARE**   1

    1.1. TECHNOLOGIES, PRODUCTS, AND APPLICATIONS   3
    1.2. THE LEGAL AND REGULATORY CHALLENGE   4

2. **CONCEPTUAL FRAMEWORK**   7

    2.1. DATA-RELATED DEFINITIONS   7
    2.2. WHAT ARE PERSON-IDENTIFIABLE DATA?   8
    2.3. PERSON-IDENTIFIABLE HEALTH DATABASES   9
    2.4. STANDARDIZATION AND PERSONAL DATA   11
    2.5. WHAT IS AN ELECTRONIC HEALTH RECORD?   11
    2.6. DECISION SUPPORT APPLICATIONS   14
    2.7. NETWORKED HEALTHCARE APPLICATIONS   15
    2.8. ELECTRONIC COMMERCE   16

3. **LEGAL AND REGULATORY ISSUES**   21

    3.1. AREAS OF LEGAL AND REGULATORY CONCERN IN THE USE OF COMPUTER-BASED HEALTH RECORDS AND DATABASES   21
    3.2. DATA RELIABILITY, SECURITY, AND PRIVACY   23
    3.3. PRIVACY AND CONFIDENTIALITY   24
    3.4. IMPLEMENTING RELIABLE, SECURE, AND PRIVATE COMPUTER SYSTEMS   27
    3.5. ELECTRONIC DOCUMENTS AND DIGITAL SIGNATURES   29
    3.6. MALPRACTICE AND STANDARDS OF CARE RELATED TO DATA UTILIZATION   30

4. **THE REGULATORY FRAMEWORK**   33

    4.1. LEGAL AND REGULATORY DOMAINS   33
    4.2. EARLY RESPONSES   34
    4.3. "PATCHWORK" REGULATION   35
    4.4. PRIVACY PROTECTION MODELS   37
    4.5. INTERNATIONAL ASPECTS OF PRIVACY AND DATABASES   40

5. **REVIEW OF REGULATORY RESPONSES: INTERNATIONAL ORGANIZATIONS**   43

    5.1. THE UNITED NATIONS GUIDELINES FOR COMPUTERIZED PERSONAL DATA FILES   43
    5.2. COUNCIL OF EUROPE'S 1981 CONVENTION FOR THE PROTECTION OF INDIVIDUALS WITH REGARD TO THE AUTOMATIC PROCESSING OF PERSONAL DATA   46
    5.3. THE ORGANIZATION FOR ECONOMIC COOPERATION AND DEVELOPMENT (OECD) GUIDELINES GOVERNING PRIVACY AND TRANSBORDER DATA FLOWS   47

6. **REVIEW OF REGULATORY RESPONSES: DATA PROTECTION IN THE EUROPEAN UNION**   53

    6.1. LEGISLATIVE INSTRUMENTS   54
    6.2. INTERACTIVE COMMUNICATIONS   61
    6.3. TRANSBORDER DATA FLOW   65
    6.4. STATUS OF IMPLEMENTATION OF DIRECTIVE 95/45/EC   66

7. REVIEW OF REGULATORY RESPONSES: NATIONAL INITIATIVES IN THE EUROPEAN UNION — **71**

7.1. AUSTRIA — 71
7.2. BELGIUM — 72
7.3. DENMARK — 72
7.4. FINLAND — 74
7.5. FRANCE — 75
7.6. GERMANY — 76
7.7. GREECE — 79
7.8. IRELAND — 80
7.9. ITALY — 82
7.10. LUXEMBOURG — 82
7.11. THE NETHERLANDS — 84
7.12. PORTUGAL — 86
7.13. SPAIN — 87
7.14. SWEDEN — 89
7.15. UNITED KINGDOM — 90

8. REVIEW OF REGULATORY RESPONSES: NATIONAL INITIATIVES IN EUROPEAN COUNTRIES NOT MEMBERS OF THE EUROPEAN UNION — **99**

8.1. BULGARIA — 99
8.2. ESTONIA — 100
8.3. GREENLAND — 102
8.4. HUNGARY — 102
8.5. ICELAND — 103
8.6. LATVIA — 105
8.7. LITHUANIA — 106
8.8. NORWAY — 107
8.9. POLAND — 108
8.10. RUSSIA — 110
8.11. SLOVAKIA — 111
8.12. SLOVENIA — 113
8.13. SWITZERLAND — 114
8.14. TURKEY — 116
8.15. UKRAINE — 117

9. REVIEW OF REGULATORY RESPONSES: NATIONAL INITIATIVES IN THE AMERICAS — **121**

9.1. ARGENTINA — 121
9.2. BRAZIL — 122
9.3. CANADA — 124
9.4. CHILE — 129
9.5 COLOMBIA — 129
9.6. MEXICO — 130
9.7. PERU — 131
9.8. UNITED STATES OF AMERICA — 133

10. REVIEW OF REGULATORY RESPONSES: NATIONAL INITIATIVES IN THE MIDDLE EAST AND AFRICA — **143**

10.1. ISRAEL — 143
10.2. SOUTH AFRICA — 144

11. REVIEW OF REGULATORY RESPONSES: NATIONAL INITIATIVES IN ASIA   147

    11.1. AUSTRALIA   147
    11.2. CHINA   151
    11.3. INDIA   155
    11.4. JAPAN   156
    11.5. SOUTH KOREA   158
    11.6. MALASYA   160
    11.7. NEW ZEALAND   161
    11.8. PHILIPPINES   163
    11.9. SINGAPORE   164
    11.10.REPUBLIC OF CHINA (TAIWAN)   165
    11.11.THAILAND   166

12. GLOBAL HARMONIZATION INITIATIVES   169

    12.1. PRIVACY IN ELECTRONIC TRANSACTIONS   170
    12.2. SELF-REGULATED HARMONIZATION   171
    12.3. USER-DRIVEN REGULATORY HARMONIZATION   175
    12.4. SPECIAL AREAS REQUIRING PROTECTION THROUGH LEGAL REGULATION   176
    12.5. IMPACT OF THE DIVERSITY OF REGULATIONS AT THE INTERNATIONAL LEVEL   177
    12.6. IMPLICATIONS FOR e-COMMERCE AND e-HEALTH   179

**13. INTERNET SOURCES ON REGULATORY AND LEGAL ISSUES
     ON DATA SECURITY AND PRIVACY**   183

    13.1. KEY RESOURCES   183
    13.2. OTHER RESOURCES   184
    13.2.1. UNITED STATES   184
    13.2.2. INTERNATIONAL   189

REFERENCES   193

1. Information and Communication Technologies in Healthcare

The development of computers, electronic databases, and interactive communications brought about significant changes in health practice and management. Health applications of information technologies and telecommunications encompass a broad and expanding domain that use the resources of many disciplines to improve the effectiveness and efficiency of healthcare processes. Thanks to the development of information and telecommunication systems and special software to support the daily administrative work of medical practitioners, computers have become an integral feature of the interactions between practitioners and their patients. They provide support for the challenging and complex interdependent clinical, public health, and administrative decisions and interventions required for individual and community healthcare practice; liberate caregivers from the traditional constraints of place and time; empower individuals to make informed choices; and change the way health practice is managed in a competitive marketplace [1, 2, 3, 4, 5, 6, 7].

During the last six years, the Global Information Infrastructure (GII) has expanded at an exponential rate. Besides the well established areas of distant consultation, message switching, access to knowledge databases, integration of providers, service management, and the transmission of still and moving medical images and biological signals, telecommunication and informatics have opened a whole new range of possibilities for better health practice [8].

The health component of the GII creates opportunities that can dramatically improve the practice of knowledge-enhanced national and international health systems; evidence-based clinical and administrative decision making; the creation of local, national, and global markets for the exchange of health products and services; decentralization of healthcare; and the improvement of individual and collective health status [9, 10, 11, 12, 13].

While formerly most information was collected in personal conversations between direct healthcare professionals and the patient, today medical practice and decision making is a spatially distributed process, involving numerous professionals and specialists. Many of these actors never meet face-to-face to discuss a case but each adds her or his own report, which is read, interpreted, and integrated by the primary practitioner responsible for the care event. In order to allow the shared use of collected data, so that different and spatially distributed healthcare units can retrieve and process such data, it is necessary that the various systems in use can communicate with each other (technical interoperability).

The increasing sophistication of information technology with its capacity to collect, analyze, and disseminate data on individuals has introduced a sense of urgency to the demand for legislation. Furthermore, new developments in medical research and care, telecommunications, advanced transportation systems, and financial transfers have dramatically increased the level of information generated by each individual. Those are facilitated by the following characteristics of technological deployment and use:

- **Globalization** - removes geographical limitations to the flow of data. The development of the Internet is perhaps the best known example of a global technology.

- **Technological Convergence** - leads to the elimination of technological barriers between systems. Modern information systems are increasingly interoperable with other systems, and can mutually exchange and process different forms of data.

- **Multi-media** - fuses many modes of transmission and expression of data and images so that information gathered in a certain form can be easily translated into other forms.

1.1.   Technologies, Products, and Applications

Information and telecommunications technologies have proven to be especially useful in the generation, storage, and retrieval of clinical and administrative patient-related documentation, particularly in the area of health records; in the operation of highly efficient integrated national health insurance and service delivery schemes; in the logistical support of provider organizations and patient services; in the provision of fast access to medical attention without travel or delays in waiting rooms; and in the seamless integration of support services such as gate-keeping, patient clinical information, scheduling, diagnostic result communication, and prescription management. Other applications that have been gaining acceptance in the last few years are those oriented toward electronic-mediated commerce, including the marketing, relationship creation, advice, prescribing, and selling of pharmaceuticals and medical devices [6, 7, 14].

Although there are many institutions that store in electronic format different components of a patient's medical or administrative record, there are many more situations in which individualized health information is being transmitted between providers and other stakeholders. Exchange of individualized patient data is common in consultations between health providers; in communications between patients and physicians; in the electronic interpretation of x-rays and medical tests and in the billing to third-party payers; in the transmission and receipt of prescriptions; in home monitoring of patients via audio, video, and data technologies; and in the evaluation of patients in clinical pharmaceutical trials. Those are but a few of the examples in which electronic health information is being used.

The fast-changing globally networked, multicultural, and multilingual interactive communications of the World Wide Web (WWW) environment has vast possibilities. The World Wide Web (WWW) offers unprecedented power to providers and end-users of healthcare information – patients, professionals, families, caregivers, educators, researchers, insurers, regulators, and policymakers – with data of unprecedented timeliness, accuracy, depth, and diversity. With increasing frequency, all types of medical information and patient-specific data are transmitted and stored in electronic format, and, as with all things in cyberspace, with levels of interactivity as yet unknown [4, 6, 7, 14, 15, 16, 17, 18, 19, 20].

1.2.   The Legal and Regulatory Challenge

Electronic databases, interactive communications, and the use of public communications via the WWW call into question national and international borders, cultural and ethical standards, regulations, and laws, which they may bypass [21, 22, 23, 24]. The very qualities that make the Internet such a rich tool for information exchange and marketplace of ideas – its decentralized structure, global reach, leveling of access to the tools of publication, immediacy of response, and ability to facilitate free-ranging interchange – also make it an exceptional channel for potential misinformation, unethical use, concealed bias, covert self-dealing, fraudulent practices, and evasion of legitimate regulation.

Less obvious are some of the serious legal issues that arise. As providers shift into cyberspace, the health law system faces challenges to its traditional approaches to regulation, quality assurance, and confidentiality. While communications between doctor and patient must be secure, legal implications go far beyond data integrity. Fully integrated electronic systems bring great efficiencies, but pose a threat to patient privacy. Issues in the area involve ethical, regulatory, and legal aspects related to machine quality of data used in clinical decision making, the protection of the privacy and confidentiality of individual data, and the exploitation and potential misuse of individual data for purposes other than personal healthcare. Authentication is another issue of major importance – the parties to electronic exchanges must be assured of the identity of the other parties – a concept at odds with the vaunted anonymity of cyberspace communications [20].

Despite the extensive use of electronic healthcare information, comprehensive regulation for this electronic medium is yet to be adopted both at country level and internationally. There are many inadequacies concerning national and international controls and legislation, especially regarding the issue of jurisdiction, and there is an urgent need for an internationally accepted policy framework that addresses basic rights and responsibilities of users, providers, and data subjects.

Freedom of access to information and expression and the protection of users' data security and privacy are especially critical topics. Decisions and initiatives related to cyberspace law and ethics issues in health and healthcare must necessarily involve experts from a variety of knowledge domains involving civil and criminal law, medical ethics (bioethics), computing ethics, medical computing, and legal medicine [19, 21, 25].

Traditionally, local standards are considered the yardstick against which health practice is evaluated, and they determine the parameters for eventual litigation. Remote conduction of health interventions and off-site databases brings forth a whole new range of questions and ethical aspects in the patient-provider relationship. Those issues have been reviewed and recommendations regarding a code of practice have been proposed [22, 24, 26]. Guidelines regarding the ethical and legal aspects of remote healthcare (telemedicine) are in the process of being developed by national and international trade, professional, and technical organizations and by national regulatory agencies. This is an area of fast changes, and an extensive review of legal aspects of telemedicine practice in the U.S. can be found in a publication by one of the authors [27].

2. Conceptual Framework

2.1. Data-related Definitions

Database - A database is a collection of records that can be created, updated, sorted, removed, searched, and subject to a number of logical operations. A database allows the storage of multiple pieces of information (data items) in one file, instead of using several files for each data item. Normally a database contains many fields of data. One can think of a field as a place in which you can hold a specific data item. The advantages of databases are that they are easy to search and conduct operations for specific items.

Identifiable Data - Any data which either directly or indirectly identify an individual by reference to his/her name, public identification numbers, or one or more factors specific to his/her physical, physiological, mental, economic, cultural, or social identity.

Personal Data - Defined as any information that relates to an identified or identifiable natural person. Personal health data encompass a wide range of information about an individual private life and include not only medical data but also sensitive data on behavioral patterns, sexual life, social and economic factors, as well as administrative data related to contacts with the healthcare system.

Data Management - Means any operation or set of operations that are performed upon personal data, whether or not by automatic means. Range of possible uses of personal health data covers all aspects of data management: collection, recording, processing, storage, access, and communication. It also includes related tasks or issues such as responsibilities, auditing, etc.

Data Controller - The natural or legal person, public authority, agency, or other body that determines, either alone or jointly with others, the purposes and means for which personal data will be processed. In healthcare the controller may be an individual practitioner or a health authority, agency, or organization. In the latter case, they have a duty to ensure that their employees comply with the existing regulatory and legal framework.

2.2.   What Are Person-identifiable Data?

The British Caldicott Report [28] identified a number of data items by which a person's identity may be established. These include:

- Surname
- Forename
- Initials
- Address
- Postal Code
- Date of Birth
- Other Dates (i.e., death, diagnosis)
- Sex
- National Health Service Number
- National Identification Number
- Local Identifier (i.e., hospital or provider identifier)
- Ethnic Group
- Soundex Code (a computer routine that permits search of individuals with similar name)
- Occupation

Any item from this list, which may not lead to the identification of an individual but, when taken with another item from a particular data set, may in certain circumstances enable identification to be inferred, for example: age linked to a diagnosis; postal code and the medicine prescribed; address and the item of service provided. While it may be helpful to consider items of information as falling within a spectrum of "identifiability" based on the nature of the item and the context, nevertheless all personal information is confidential and deserves the same respect for privacy.

Except for national identifiers (in the case of the United Kingdom, the National Health Service Number), no single item can be relied upon uniquely to identify an individual and the degree to which other items might identify an individual will depend on the context – for example an unusual surname may be a stronger pointer to an individual than a more common surname.

2.3. Person-identifiable Health Databases

The emergence of health databanks to support electronic health records, networked and decision support application, and health e-commerce has raised serious data security and privacy concerns. There is growing consensus that the creation, maintenance, and operation of databases containing individual patient data must be subject to regulations [29, 30, 31, 32].

In many countries, proposals and actual reform of the laws have been introduced according to which individuals are entitled to know what information is stored, who accessed a particular database containing person-identifiable information, what use was made of the particular set of data accessed, and what mechanisms are available to correct erroneous information. The purpose of these regulations is to guarantee that medical data are used in a secure and ethical manner ensuring optimum medical care and services that fully respects the data subject's dignity and rights [33, 34, 35].

Health database regulations and standards being proposed or implemented contain provisions on:

- Specific purpose(s);

- Finality of purpose;

- Categories of information recorded;

- Body or person for and by whom the database is established and operated;

- Who is competent to decide which categories of data should be processed;

- Person(s) in charge of the day-to-day operation;

- Person(s) in charge of privacy maintenance and ethical utilization;

- Categories of persons who are entitled to cause data to be placed in storage, modified, and erased ("originators of the data");

- Person(s) or body to whom certain decisions must be submitted for approval, supervision of use, and to whom appeal may be made in the event of dispute;

- Categories of persons who have access to the data bank in the course of their work and the categories of data to which they are entitled to have access;

- Disclosure of information to third parties;

- Disclosure of information to the individuals concerned ("data subjects");

- Rights of data subjects to have errors corrected or data segments removed from their record;

- Long-term conservation of data; procedure concerning requests for use of data for purpose other than those for which they have been collected;

- Mechanisms for physical security of data and installations; and

- Whether and on which conditions the linkage with other data banks is permitted.

It is also recognized, however, that the strict application of rules based on some of the above provisions may cause difficulties to clinical practice, lead to poor individual patient care, and paradoxically even be responsible for unethical situations, e.g., creating barriers for a professional to assess data related to a patient under his/her care.

2.4. Standardization and Personal Data

The design of information and telecommunication systems and network technology influences which personal health data are collected, stored, and maintained and who should or could have access to them. One main effect of the development of such technologies is the globalization of standards and procedures, which may be used, for example, in the determination of protocols for diagnosis and treatment. Standards and protocols can serve as tools for good practice [13] and constitute an important component of quality assurance.

The collection of standardized data and the use of such protocols require, however, that the practitioner/patient interaction must be structured according to a pre-set format. Standards are not neutral – they embody the ethical, social, economic, political, and epistemological choices of their creators and will necessarily favor or reject particular views of patients or diseases [30].

2.5. What Is an Electronic Health Record?

What initially may sound like a simplistic question regarding what constitutes an Electronic Health Record (EHR) quickly becomes a complex issue. Though there is often general agreement that an EHR contains patient-specific information about an individual's medical or health status and related administrative and financial data, the particular structure and contents of such records are seldom agreed upon. This is due to the differing uses to which a medical record can be put, as well as the wide variety of entities and health professionals using it.

Consider a short recitation of the various healthcare entities for which an electronic medical record could be useful: physician offices, hospital inpatient and outpatient services, community clinics, managed care organizations, health maintenance organizations, ambulance services, home health agencies, nursing homes, government agencies, health insurance companies, assisted living facilities, pharmacies, and durable medical equipment suppliers. Depending upon the intended use of the EHR, it may contain patient's detailed clinical data in textual and non-textual (image, voice, recordings of biomedical signals) formats such as diagnosis, family history, past and present health problems, allergies, genetic markers, description of physical examination findings, x-rays, and a multitude of historical diagnostic test results and extensive administrative data such as insurance company information, employer status, health plan coverage numbers and levels of benefits, dependent information, billing codes, address, contact information, and past profile of health service utilization including economic data related to procedures and treatment.

Compounding the difficulties of reaching a consensus on a set of common data elements are the numerous medical specialties and the variances in information that each specialty or sub-specialty requires or prefers. There is, therefore, a broad spectrum of desired information and how it is presented and used among healthcare providers and organizations. The medical information required by a hospital emergency department may differ from that sought in a pediatric group practice environment, or the needs of a psychiatric practice are likely to be quite different from information needed by an obstetrician, or the data gathered by one of the service branches of the armed forces will certainly be different from the medical information sought by a healthcare insurer. Though not impossible, reaching a consensus on the core information to be obtained for a "common medical record" is difficult, at best.

Differences in software and hardware platforms and communication technologies can present barriers to connectivity between institutions and providers, as there are currently no rules obligating all health institutions to use identical, or even compatible, technology. In fact, rapidly developing technological advancements appear to make the standardization of equipment, and interoperability, more difficult in many instances. Just as there are a vast number of healthcare professionals and entities using electronic health information, there are also a plethora of different platforms or templates being used to gather, transmit, store, and retrieve electronic health information.

Electronic cards containing integrated circuit non-volatile memory can hold all or a subset of an individual's record and can be seen as a "portable" component of the computer-based record. Such cards may exist either as a practitioner-held card or, more commonly, as a patient-held card. Some European countries are currently testing or deploying publicly accessible card-reading facilities (kiosks) through which citizens may have direct or indirect access to stored data [36].

Many countries and health organizations are already routinely utilizing some form of computerized or electronic health record in various ways and for different purposes. Physicians, clinics, hospitals, insurers, managed care organizations, pharmacies, government agencies, and other entities have been using patient-specific electronic health information in connection with the delivery of healthcare services, healthcare financing, or health services research. Group providers and healthcare organizations in the United States (Kaiser-Permanente, Mayo Clinic, Veterans Administration, Department of Defense, Louisiana State University Medical Center, Indiana University School of Medicine, Columbia Presbyterian Medical Center) have implemented partial or "complete" EHR applications. Electronic health records have also been extensively investigated and deployed in the European Community; a review of EU projects was published in 1995 [37], including the broad deployment of "smart-cards" as a portable component of the computer-based record.

Regarding health records alone, there are scores of commercial products and service providers offering a great variety of functionalities, capabilities, and hardware and software platform options. In the 1999 Resource Guide published by *Healthcare Informatics*, a leading U.S. publication, 192 companies were listed as providing electronic health record products or services [38]. Vendors list their products and services under a variety of names: Automated Medical Record, Computerized Medical Record, Computerized Patient Record, Computer-based Patient Record, Electronic Patient Record, Electronic Health Record, Virtual Health Record, etc. Also, over the past five years there has been a growing number of companies marketing the ASP (Web-based Application Service Provider) model of information services offering partial or full Internet hosting for medical records, including the possibility of off-site storage. The ASP model makes possible cost sharing, economy of scale, and minimal in-house informatics and manpower infrastructure but at the same time, raises a number of security and confidentiality issues.

Project development and characteristics of applications have been directly related to local needs and desired functions and results. Software products have a great variety of features and there is much discussion regarding the structure, contents, and standards adopted by electronic patient record applications. Specification options adopted by different developers have not been standardized, and the most complex problem has been the design of a truly comprehensive longitudinal record that can be reliably accessed online at any point of care. Unfortunately, in most cases, there has been no benchmarking for quality and appropriateness of implemented solutions.

Critical issues in implementing electronic health record applications are related to the need to satisfy the form of work and habits of physicians and nurses in a great variety of environments and guaranteeing systems availability, the support of transactions among different users located in diverse geographical locations, response time in data search and retrieval, and the customizability of the EHR for different specialties and tasks. Functioning and accessible workstations in every point of care or wireless mobile handheld devices are required in most cases with the concurrent costs of deploying and maintaining such configurations. Extant projects around the world have been evaluated and experts have been unanimously of the opinion that the implementation of the EHR must be done in the context of a global reorganization of the healthcare processes, including the change to a patient-centric rather than facility-centric model of service provision.

2.6. Decision Support Applications

Clinical decision software applications are designed to support the analysis of patient data and to automate aspects of clinical decision making that can be expressed as rules. Such rules can be built and maintained by a database of guidelines and the legal implications of the mainstream introduction and use of clinical decision-support software are many and far-reaching. Concerns raised involve questions such as:

- When does the amount of automated "clinical thinking" done by the software application constitute "practice of medicine" with all its associated ethical and legal aspects?

- Is a decision-support software to be considered a medical device passive of regulation?

- To what extent does the application software allow clinicians to examine the underlying logic and to independently evaluate how the software arrived at particular conclusions?

- What is the role of such products in critical clinical decisions?

- How are the consequences of eventual errors to be dealt with?

Many of those issues have not yet been addressed. They are important in light of the fact that the health information technology industry is investing millions of dollars in developing such applications. Developments on a number of policy, legislation, and regulation issues are badly needed in this area. Medical software is increasingly considered as another form of medical device.

2.7. Networked Healthcare Applications

Networked systems, in the form of intranets, extranets, and the public space of the Internet, facilitate communication among health stakeholders. Networked interactive communication technologies are shaping the future of healthcare. They reinforce, complement, and enhance existing health programs and healthcare delivery systems, offer new solutions for health interventions, and create the opportunity for the establishment and operation of innovative practice models. Telemedicine or Telehealth is a prime example of such applications that include: consultation services and remote care; clinical, epidemiological, and administrative data management and communication; provision of diagnostic and therapeutic services; image-based systems; integration of distributed providers; access to knowledge databases and decision support tools; education and training through interactive communication media; health promotion; and the management of physical and financial resources [14, 39, 40, 41, 42].

For health lawyers, the most immediate concerns are related to licensure and how data are maintained and used. Healthcare professionals are regulated by state- or region-based licensing systems. Yet cyberspace is oblivious to such "real world" jurisdictional demarcations or limitations. Systems intrinsic complexity and the use of public telecommunication networks and commercial software frequently plagued by security flaws make it difficult to implement and maintain unfailing and consistent data integrity, reliability, and confidentiality in such systems.

2.8. Electronic Commerce

Electronic commerce involves business-to-business communication, business-to-consumer communication, and business-to-government communication. With regard to legal implications of electronic commerce there are a vast array of issues and laws applicable to the Internet stressing the importance of a contractual agreement and the validity of forming contractual relationships electronically, raising the question of digital signatures as a valid way of authenticating a document. There are many administrative requirements imposed upon organizations in terms of form and record keeping. In the United Kingdom, for instance, Companies House advises that it is good practice to supply every e-mail message sent out with the company registered name, address, and company registration number. New regulations make it a criminal offense not to do so when sending e-mail to shareholders.

On a European level, recent legislation in the framework of the Directive 2000/31/EC on Electronic Commerce [43] provides for certain basic standards to improve the legal situation of both the consumer and provider of electronic commerce services. It established basic rules on transparency, requiring Member States to obligate Information Society service providers to make available to customers and competent authorities basic information concerning their activities (name, address, e-mail address, trade registration number, professional authorization and membership of professional bodies where applicable, and VAT number) in an easily accessible and permanent form.

Of great importance to providers of Internet services and in order to eliminate existing legal uncertainties and to avoid divergent approaches between Member States, the Directive establishes an exemption from liability for intermediaries where they play a passive role as a "mere conduit" of information from third parties and limits service providers' liability for other "intermediary" activities such as the storage of information. The Directive strikes a careful balance between the different interests involved in order to stimulate cooperation between different parties and so reduce the risk of illegal activity online.

The use of electronic networks for commerce creates information trails that allow customers' transaction information to be easily tracked, collected, and compiled, providing others with the personal details of people's lives. Supermarkets and other retail establishments use scanners that allow purchases to be tracked. Bank and credit card companies have information about payment histories, where people shop, and what transactions are conducted and what goods and services are acquired. Insurance companies, doctors, and hospitals have vast amounts of personal information about their clients and patients. The ease with which personal information can be collected, compiled, and transmitted can, if not managed carefully, interfere with personal privacy. Thus, information privacy – an individual's control over the manner in which personal information is obtained, disclosed, and used – is critical to the development and use of electronic commerce.

Global electronic commerce invokes cross-border issues and the need for harmonization. This is all the more important in view of the emergence of market partitioning due to a legal insecurity that companies are facing in electronic commerce. The question is how to balance the flexibility given to companies to make a contractual choice of law and an obligation to apply the overriding rules of law.

There are many issues of protection and notification of government and third parties, topics related to business processes such as self-billing and self-invoicing, the question of liability of the growing number of intermediaries that appear in an open electronic environment, i.e., trusted third parties, certification authorities, Internet payment service providers, anonymous remailers, Internet service providers, etc.

There are two distinct sides of the data protection aspect in electronic commerce: personal data collected in traditional mechanisms and made available over the Internet, and data protection issues arising from monitoring of online activities. In the health sector e-commerce applications electronically process claims, patient data, and prescription information and exchange such data among managed care organizations, hospitals, physicians, pharmaceutical companies, and other suppliers. More visible are so-called vertical portals, web sites structured to appeal to particular subsets of web users. Vertical portals, aimed at physicians, feature clinical information and specialty interaction, while selling advertising, books, and continuing medical education services. Vertical portals aimed at patients marry consumer-oriented health information to online consultations, prescription drug fulfillment, and related services and products. Current generation sites deliver "advice" in one of three ways: generalized textual content or "frequently asked questions" (FAQs), open forums for discussions, and personalized interactive sessions (by chat or e-mail) with site experts [44, 45, 46].

In most states, the question will arise as to which, if any, of these activities entail the practice of medicine and so implicate licensure and, ultimately, unlicensed practice. The answer may be relatively simple in the case of a one-to-one interaction between physician and patient that leads to prescribing a drug. However, more generalized interactions are far harder to characterize. A related issue has arisen regarding the practice of pharmacy across state lines and, specifically, web-based pharmacies. As an example, the states of Illinois and Kansas in the U.S. specifically regulate electronic transactions and are attempting to prosecute out-of-state pharmacies and associated medical professionals and bring into effect federal regulation and enforcement by the Food and Drug Administration (FDA) and the Drug Enforcement Agency (DEA).

Internet service providers and those who web-publish content provided by others generally are immune from liability. As a result, sites that merely aggregate or link to the content of others are unlikely to be liable for negligent medical advice. However, sites that create their own content will have liability exposure. No doubt these sites will rely on various tort and constitutional law decisions that traditionally have protected authors and publishers. However, those decisions may not apply in cases where direct relationships between health professionals and patients have been established or where a site delivers highly targeted or personalized content. Overall, sites confront extremely complex risk management issues. For example, in the U.S. malpractice insurance typically is written on a state-by-state basis suggesting considerable difficulties for physicians practicing in cyberspace.

Health lawyers may also be forced to change their concept of the medical malpractice defendant. In the real world, health law frequently differentiates physicians, institutions, and manufacturers, often applying discrete legal rules to them. However, cyberspace frequently obscures the nature of the underlying business. For example, is the advice coming from a doctor or a drug company? Furthermore, the transition to cyberspace may radically change the traditionally regulated health business models. Business models that were once independent, for example the doctor and pharmacy, may be integrated online. Equally, services like the sale and delivery of a prescription drug that traditionally have been integrated may become independent.

3. Legal and Regulatory Issues

3.1. Areas of Legal and Regulatory Concern in the Use of Computer-Based Health Records and Databases

Electronic health records applications raise a number of legal and regulatory questions that are frequently intertwined:

Access. How does the electronic transmission and storage system limit the access to computer-based medical records and identifiable personal data in health databases to only those with a legitimate reason for use? Is access to health information restricted according to classes of personnel (e.g., clinical versus billing), types of information (e.g., mental health and substance abuse), or differing locations (e.g., central hub versus remote location, or home health agency versus hospital)?

Tracking. Is the system capable of tracking those with access to, and use of, the system and is an audit trail available if needed for future verification, discipline, or enforcement? Can misdirected communications be identified and tracked? Can the tracking system cope with the occasional need to correct data or remove incorrect data in such a way that invalid data is no longer visible on the face of the record, but that its correction or erasure is properly tracked?

Interoperability. Are the various systems used by connected institutions, entities, and providers capable of interacting and "speaking with" each other? If an electronic medical record stored at one institution or locale is to be transmitted to a second institution, will the two systems be compatible and able to exchange the information without corrupting or deleting the content data?

Common Data Sets. Is the information gathered by each institution or provider sufficient for, and usable by, other institutions to which the information is transmitted? Health insurers, hospitals, clinics, researchers and various medical providers each use specific information in unique ways and, in some instances, information obtained by one may be insufficient or inadequate for use by the other.

Information Integrity. Are the electronic transmission, storage and retrieval system adequate to protect against data corruption, alteration, and deletion? Once accurate information has been inserted, can it be safely transmitted, received, stored and retrieved without unintended alteration, corruption, and deletion?

Privacy. Will the information be used and stored in such a way that the sensitive and private nature of its contents will be protected, disclosed only upon proper authorization?

Confidentiality. Will the information be accessible only by authorized users with a legitimate need? The system needs to safeguard the confidential nature of the health information to ensure that the confidential nature of the information itself, and the communication between patient and provider, is not eroded by improper disclosure.

Security. Does the electronic medical record system protect against unauthorized intruders, both in intranet systems (within a single institution or group of entities) as well as internet systems (between various unrelated entities)?

Storage and Retrieval. Can the system safely store the information in a form capable of timely retrieval without impairing the integrity of information?

Sender Verification and Encryption. Can the receiver of transmitted electronic information verify the authenticity of the sender as a guard against fraudulent information? Is encryption used and, if so, are necessary recipients able to access such information?

Data Replication. In instances where patients carry electronic health information with them between providers, who bears the responsibility for updating the electronic record if subsequent examinations, treatments, and procedures are undertaken? Will transported electronic records be readable by destination entities?

Dispute Resolution. For parties wishing to pursue legal redress, what forum is vested with jurisdiction? What alternatives are available for parties involved in electronic transmission of health information to resolve disputes arising from the transmission, corruption, deletion, improper disclosure, alteration, and retention of electronic health records? Additionally, what country's laws govern and, if state or other local laws apply, what local laws are applicable? What agencies of various countries have responsibility and authority for enforcement of relevant laws?

Scalability. Can the existing technology be expanded into a greater scope of capability without totally replacing the existing system? Is it possible to add additional features to the system without reconstructing it as a whole?

Sanction and Penalty Enforcement. If jurisdiction for dispute resolution is vested with a specific agency, tribunal, commission or other body, does the same body possess sufficient authority and power to enforce penalties or sanctions that are imposed? Does the authority for enforcement arise from treaties or agreements agreed upon by the parties, or by operation of law?

3.2. Data Reliability, Security, and Privacy

There is a growing concern regarding the protection of identifiable personal health records against intrusion, unauthorized use, data corruption, intentional or unintentional damage, theft, and fraud. Given the sensitive nature of healthcare information, and the high degree of dependence of health professionals on reliable records, the issues of reliability, security, and privacy are of particular significance and must be clearly and effectively addressed by health and health-related organizations and professionals.

- **Reliability** - Data residing in the electronic health record is accurate and remains accurate.

- **Security** - Owner and users of the electronic health record can control data transmission and storage.

- **Privacy** - The subject of data can control its use and dissemination.

Reliability, security, and privacy are accomplished by the implementation of a number of preventive and protective policies, tools, and actions that address the following areas:

- **Physical Protection** - Protection against intentional or accidental damage.

- **Integrity** - Prevention of unauthorized modification of information.

- **Access** - Prevention of unauthorized entry into information resources.

- **Confidentiality** - Protection against unauthorized disclosure of information.

3.3.   Privacy and Confidentiality

Unquestionably, legal concerns about privacy are the most pressing and immediate source of disquiet in the use of health electronic records and personal databases. Privacy can be defined as a fundamental though not an absolute human right. Privacy can be defined as the ability of people to choose freely under what circumstances and to what extent they will expose themselves, their attitude, and their behavior to others.

Privacy is an interest of the human personality and it protects the inviolate personality, the individual's independence, dignity, and integrity. Privacy underpins human dignity and other key values such as freedom of association and freedom of speech. It has become one of the most important human rights issues of the modern age.

The law of privacy can be traced as far back as 1361, during the reign of Edward III, when the Justices of the Peace Act was introduced in England and provided for the arrest of peeping toms and eavesdroppers [47]. Privacy is a right recognized in all major international treaties and agreements. It is recognized in the United Nations Declaration of Human Rights and the International Covenant on Civil and Political Rights (ICCPR), the United Nations Convention on Migrant Workers, the United Nations Convention on Protection of the Child, and in many other international and regional treaties.

The modern privacy benchmark at an international level can be found in the 1948 Universal Declaration of Human Rights, which specifically protected territorial and communications privacy. Article 12 states: "No-one should be subjected to arbitrary interference with his privacy, family, home or correspondence, nor to attacks on his honor or reputation. Everyone has the right to the protection of the law against such interference or attacks" [48].

In 1965, the Organization of the American States (OAS) proclaimed the American Declaration of the Rights and Duties of Man, which called for the protection of numerous human rights including privacy [49]. The Inter-American Court of Human Rights has also begun to addresses privacy issues in its cases.

Nearly every country in the world recognizes privacy as a fundamental human right in its constitution, either explicitly or implicitly. New technologies are increasingly posing threats to privacy rights. There is a growing trend towards the enactment of comprehensive privacy and data protection acts around the world. Currently over forty countries and jurisdictions have or are in the process of enacting such laws. Countries are adopting these laws to promote electronic exchanges and to ensure compatibility with international standards, the most comprehensive being the ones developed by the European Union, the Council of Europe, and the Organization for Economic Cooperation and Development (OECD).

Most recently enacted constitutions such as South Africa's and Hungary's include specific rights to access and control one's personal information. In many of the countries where privacy is not explicitly recognized in the constitution, such as the United States, Ireland and India, the courts have found that right in other provisions. In many countries, international agreements that recognize privacy rights such as the International Covenant on Civil and Political Rights or the European Convention on Human Rights have been adopted into law [50].

Privacy involves many aspects, and the issue has been consistently one of the top concern of users and has given rise to fears related to confidentiality, right of access, and intended use of personal data. In many countries, proposals and actual reform of the laws have been enacted, according to which individuals are entitled to know what information is stored about them, who accessed it, and what mechanisms are available to correct erroneous information [30, 31, 32, 42, 43, 44, 45, 46, 50, 51].

Trust – the firm reliance on the integrity, ability, or character of a person or service and the condition and resulting obligation of having confidence placed in a healthcare provider – is a core aspect of the provider-patient relationship. Patients explicitly or implicitly grant their providers permission to use their personal data in an appropriate and ethical manner to support care delivery. Ethical medical practice dictates that a patient's privacy rights and preferences must be protected by all users of person-identifiable health information. Most experts concur that fundamentally all decisions about the use and disclosure of personal health information must be made and mutually agreed upon by the patient and the care provider [39].

The core principle of confidentiality has been the focal point of medical ethics since the time of Hippocrates. In more recent times, it has been developed by various codes, including the International Code of Medical Ethics. The United Kingdom General Medical Council, which oversees the registration of medical practitioners and supervises the practice of medicine in the U.K., has issued guidance on the protection of medical information in its booklet [52], published as part of a series on good medical practice. It restates the Hippocratic principle by stating that: "Patients have a right to expect that you will not disclose any personal information which you learn during the course of your professional duties, unless they give permission. Without assurances about confidentiality patients may be reluctant to give doctors the information they need in order to provide good care. For these reasons, when you are responsible for confidential information you must make sure that the information is effectively protected against improper disclosure when it is disposed of, stored, transmitted or received."

Similar statements have been made elsewhere in Europe, including: Belgium by the National Council of the Order of Physicians, the Netherlands by the Royal Dutch Society for the Advancement of Medicine, Ireland by the Irish Medical Council, Italy by the National Federation of Medical Doctors, Surgeons and Obstetricians, and in Germany by the German Medical Association.

3.4. Implementing Reliable, Secure, and Private Computer Systems

Implementation of reliable, secure, and private computer-based records is not an easy task. By their very nature there is an inherent high security and privacy risk in healthcare organizations due to the nature of distributed environments and large number of professionals and clerical staff with a variety of need to know privileges and authority. Interdisciplinary activities, multiprofessional care, remote storage and access to clinical and administrative health record data, and right to use by clerical staff (payers, controllers, insurers) require unencumbered access to identifiable individual patient data.

Health data transmitted over national and international networks offer unprecedented opportunities for better patient care and community health interventions by facilitating data exchange among professionals but pose difficult new challenges to confidentiality. An illegitimate user could attempt to gain access to a computer system connected to a network or illegally intercept a transmission. Although systems can be made more secure by restricting access to sites and encrypting information, any security solution will have to be a compromise between the need to protect information and the need to allow access to it.

Health practice, by itself, has specific needs that may create conflicts in the implementation of reliability, security, and privacy measures:

- Reliability and privacy require security, but the implementation of many data security solutions may impair privacy.

- Patients may be unable to consent to information disclosure due to their health condition. This may be especially critical in acute situations.

- In some cases, such as diseases of compulsory notification, it may be in the interests of public health to record disease incidence notwithstanding the refusal of consent by the patient.

- Clinically anonymous information is useless to direct healthcare professionals dealing with a specific patient.

- Differently than in other areas (e.g., national security and defense) where it is more acceptable to lose information than to risk exposure, in the health sector it is preferable to expose information, even running the risk of violating privacy, rather than miss information that is critical for appropriate healthcare.

- In the healthcare sector the responsibility is widely distributed among different stakeholders.

- While it is important to establish a complete audit trial of medical records, it may also be desirable in some cases to be able to correct a record leaving no visible trace of the previous data or related data entry event.

- Security is a multidimensional problem that must be solved for each specific situation, not as a generic technical add-on.

- Although it is acceptable that data in transit should be encrypted, data in use must be decrypted and may reside as such in systems with minimal access control and security.

The implementation of high-level security procedures and technological solutions in the healthcare environment must be unobtrusive and should be balanced to the operational requirements of health professionals – for example, in many clinical circumstances timely access is essential; whereas cumbersome security and privacy routines may impair patient care. Most security violations are unintentional and most damaging violations are internal to the organization, operator's error being the most frequent reason. Finally, health professionals, healthcare organizations, and the society in general must address the issue of how to balance the need for access, integrity, and privacy issues of individual rights versus the collective needs of public and community health.

3.5. Electronic Documents and Digital Signatures

Electronic networks to which the general public have direct access, such as the Internet, are becoming increasingly popular as a means of worldwide communication between healthcare professionals and as a method by which patients can become better informed about their health and treatment options. It is impossible to deny that the many possible uses of electronic documents in healthcare raise new and important questions regarding their legal validity, including the verification of document authenticity and contents. In paper-based systems, when a physician writes a prescription and the patient takes it to the pharmacist, the pharmacist will know if it has been authorized by a genuine medical practitioner because it will contain that practitioner's signature and stamp. The issue is, how can we create the same kind of certainty and security if we send the prescription to the pharmacist electronically, by e-mail for instance?

In order to use computer networks for communication we need to be able to digitally "sign" documents in a way that not only guarantees the sender that it can be read only by its intended recipient (confidentiality), but also informs the recipient who the document is from (identity), ensures that the document has not been altered in any way (integrity), and provides evidence of the signer's intent (non-repudiation). This can be done by advanced encryption methods such as public key cryptography (PKC), wherein mathematically related keys are generated.

Another option is to use a commonly trusted third party to validate user identities. This solution is convenient for users that are not known to each other or communicate infrequently through an open network – a situation where there will not be an adequate level of trust between them or in the security of their method of communication. A trusted third party is a person or institution not directly involved in the communication, but trusted by the recipient of a message to check and confirm the identity of the sender. For example, a trusted third party, known as a "certification authority", can make public keys available to anyone that needs to verify the digital signature of another person.

The usefulness of digital signatures, carried, for instance, on a smartcard, as a means of making "untrusted" networks sufficiently secure to transmit electronic healthcare documents is obvious – but their utility greatly depends upon the legal acceptability of electronic documents and digital signatures. Legal approaches to electronic documents and digital signatures vary enormously between countries. In countries where digital signatures are not recognized as being legally valid, i.e., of equivalence to a hand-written signature, electronic healthcare records may not be acceptable. Some countries already have a national legal framework that defines "documents" and "signatures" generically enough for digital signatures and electronic documents to be accepted without the need for new legislation, while others view electronic documents and digital signatures as completely new concepts, for which new laws must be enacted. In this latter category France, Germany and Italy have comprehensive legislation governing the use of electronic documents and digital signatures [21].

3.6. Malpractice and Standards of Care Related to Data Utilization

The duty of the medical practitioner is to provide care that is responsible, correct, and appropriate to the circumstances. If the means, technical or intellectual, normally used by a competent and diligent professional have not been used, this represents negligence.

Although the legal systems in different countries vary in the laws that they apply to the question of whether or not a healthcare professional has been negligent, the same basic principle underpins these approaches – in general, a health professional will not be guilty of malpractice where he or she has acted in accordance with a practice accepted as proper by a responsible body of professionals, skilled in that particular art, provided reasonable skill and care have been used. Malpractice – as applied to all of the actions a healthcare professional may undertake including the warning of risks, obtaining of valid consent, making a diagnosis, and selecting appropriate treatment – is, therefore, judged by reference to the existence of a legal duty and the acceptable standards of practice that must be met [27].

Hence a consultant using data transmitted by an electronic network will not have been negligent if he acted in accordance with a standard of practice accepted by a group of consultants that use the same technology, notwithstanding that the group may be numerically small and that a contrary body of opinion may exist, provided that the standard can withstand logical analysis [21]. Given that there are still few instances of fully integrated telecommunications-based patient care (telemedicine) services being used, the problem faced by malpractice litigation is related to what standards are acceptable.

The issue of standards needs to be dealt with by two separate lines of enquiry. Firstly we must ask whether or not it is standard practice to use telemedicine at all in the field in question – while radiology, dermatology and pathology already employ such tools on a regular basis, its acceptance by other branches of medicine has been much slower. Secondly, to complicate matters, there are many conflicts between existing regulations of medical practice and potential malpractice situations and the interest of patients.

The "four-principles" approach of Beauchamp and Childress [53] to bioethics includes respect for justice in the allocation of medical resources as one of the fundamental ethical principles of medical practice. But converting a perceived moral obligation to achieve equity in health resource allocation into a legally imposed determination that health professionals are obligated to provide access to the highest standard of medical care simply by virtue of a patient's geographical isolation is a difficult proposition [21, 22].

Regarding the protection of data, data controllers and users must implement appropriate technical and organizational measures to protect personal data against accidental or unlawful destruction or accidental loss, alteration, unauthorized disclosure or access, in particular where the processing involves the transmission of data over a network, and against all other forms of processing. Also there are specific responsibilities incumbent upon telecommunications service providers to protect the privacy of data subjects [26, 27, 29] and companies, such as healthcare organizations and pharmaceutical industries when using an individual's information, including proper notice, access, and enforcement.

4. The Regulatory Framework

4.1. Legal and Regulatory Domains

The legal and regulatory issues arising from information systems and technology applications in health and healthcare involve the intersection of four knowledge areas: ethics, law, biomedicine, and computing. In considering the nature of the pertinent legal and regulatory questions the following two-way intersections are concerned: civil and criminal law, medical ethics (bioethics), computing ethics, medical computing, and legal medicine. Those intersections correspond to the prime domain of interest and action of cyberspace law and regulation (Figure 1).

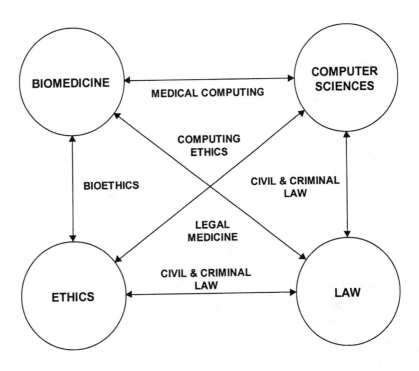

Figure 1. Knowledge Domains Related to Health Information and Communications Legal and Regulatory Issues

Because of the broad range of expertise required to deal with questions and situations related to cyberspace law and regulation any decision or initiative should involve professionals of all main and related (intersection areas) knowledge areas concerned.

4.2. Early Responses

Interest in the right of privacy increased in the 1960s and 1970s with the advent of information technology. The surveillance potential of powerful computer systems prompted demands for specific rules governing the collection and handling of personal information. In many countries, new constitutions reflect this demand. The genesis of modern legislation in this area can be traced to the first data protection law in the world enacted in the Land of Hesse in Germany in 1970. This was followed by national laws in Sweden (1973), the United States (1974), Germany (1977), and France (1978) [54].

Three crucial international instruments evolved from these laws: the Council of Europe's 1981 Convention for the Protection of Individuals with regard to the Automatic Processing of Personal Data [55], the Organization for Economic Cooperation and Development's (OECD) Guidelines Governing the Protection of Privacy and Transborder Data Flows of Personal Data [56], and the United Nations Guidelines for Computerized Personal Data Files 1990 [57]. They articulated specific rules covering the handling of electronic data, and the rules set forth by these two documents form the core of the data protection laws of dozens of countries.

These rules describe personal information and data that are afforded protection at every step from collection through to storage and dissemination. The right of people to access and amend their data is a primary component of these rules. The expression of data protection in various declarations and laws varies only by degrees. All require that personal information must be:

- Obtained fairly and lawfully;

- Used only for the original specified purpose;

- Adequate, relevant, and not excessive to purpose;

- Accurate and up to date; and

- Destroyed after its purpose is completed.

These agreements and the Directives of the European Union that followed have had a profound effect on the adoption of laws around the world. The Data Protection Directive (95/46/EC) sets a benchmark for national legislation that will harmonize law throughout the European Union [33]. Each European Union Member State was required to pass complementary legislation by October 1998 but the process is still ongoing.

The Telecommunications Privacy Directive 97/66/EC of 1997 [58] establishes specific protections covering telephone, digital television, mobile networks, and other telecommunications systems. . It should be noted however that this Directive is currently in the process of being updated within the context of the proposals to strengthen competition in the electronic communications market. In order to achieve this goal, the existing bundle of twenty-eight regulatory measures in telecommunications will be simplified and reduced to eight, with a specific and technology neutral Directive on Data Protection in Telecommunications which will replace the current Directive 97/66/EC.

With both Data Protection Directives, the European Union is concerned that data subjects have rights that are enshrined in explicit rules, and that they can go to a person or an authority that can act on their behalf. Every Member State will have a Privacy Commissioner or agency that enforces the rules. It is expected that the countries with which Europe does business will have to have a similar level of oversight.

4.3. "Patchwork" Regulation

Except for the standardization effort of the European Community and the OECD countries, each country's legislative, executive and judicial systems are addressing electronic health data regulation in differing ways. Complicating the present patchwork system of laws is the lack of uniformity in the area of electronic health information. A comprehensive and consistent worldwide regulation is still far in the future.

Laws have been promulgated in many countries to address specific areas, including medical information, health information, financial matters, confidentiality, privacy, e-commerce, and cyber-crime. Many countries have adopted parts of the European framework, and the OECD guidelines have also been widely used in national legislation, even outside the OECD countries. Though portions of some may affect certain segments of the healthcare industry, none offer a comprehensive regulatory scheme covering all facets of electronic health data. As a result, no country to date has enacted a single piece of legislation that offers sweeping coverage of electronic healthcare information and, in most countries, there is no single agency with oversight responsibility in this area. Instead, multiplicity of legislation and regulatory agencies appears to be the rule.

Differences between national approaches are apparent at present in laws, bills, or proposals for legislation as they refer to aspects such as the scope of legislation, the emphasis placed on different elements of protection, the detailed implementation of the data protection principles indicated above, and the machinery of enforcement.

In the United States, for instance, there are a number of government entities with responsibility for some aspect of electronic health information. Depending upon the particular circumstances, it may involve the United States Department of Justice (DOJ), the Federal Trade Commission (FTC), the United States Department of Health and Human Services (HHS), and the Health Care Financing Administration (HCFA), as all exercise some degree of electronic health data and health record responsibility. Additionally, each of the fifty states, and the District of Columbia, within the United States, is empowered to legislate concerning the use of electronic medical information within its relevant jurisdiction. Individuals and organizations seeking to comply with the existing rules and regulations are confronted with a multitude of statutes, numerous agencies, and often several jurisdictions that they must consult.

The transmission of health data between states in the United States, as well as between countries, generates profound legal and operational questions. Sending and receiving health information between countries raise profound legal and regulatory questions pertaining to how various rules might apply. While the transmission, receipt, storage, and disclosure of health information within a designated country may clearly invoke the application of relevant laws, these same activities conducted between countries can present significant problems of interpretation. For example, a medical record sent from the United States to Brazil for an electronic or telemedicine consultation might be subject to one set of mandatory disclosures (e.g., without patient consent) in the United States and a different set of conditions in Brazil. Could someone in the United States then successfully request from Brazil the disclosure of records that were prohibited in the United States? Similarly, medical record access limitations may vary substantially from country to country, thereby exposing a multinational patient's health record to differing regulations.

4.4. Privacy Protection Models

There are four major models for privacy protections. In some countries a combination of different models are used simultaneously.

Comprehensive Legislative Regulation - The regulatory model adopted by Europe, Australia, Hong Kong, New Zealand, Central and Eastern Europe, and Canada is that of a public official who enforces a comprehensive data protection law. This official, known variously as a Commissioner, Ombudsman or Registrar, monitors compliance with the law and conducts investigations into alleged breaches. The official is also responsible for public education and international liaison in data protection and data transfer. This is the preferred model for most countries adopting data protection law. It is also the model favored by Europe to ensure compliance with its new data protection regime. However, the powers of the commissions vary greatly and many report a serious lack of resources to adequately enforce the laws.

Sectoral Regulation - Some countries such as the United States have avoided general data protection rules in favor of specific sectoral laws governing, for example, video rental records and financial privacy. In such cases, enforcement is achieved through a range of mechanisms. The problem with this approach is that it requires that new legislation be introduced with each new technology, so protections frequently lag behind. The lack of legal protections for genetic information in the United States is a striking example of its limitations. In other countries, sectoral laws are used to complement a comprehensive legislation by providing more detailed protections for certain categories of information, such as police files or consumer credit records.

Self-regulation - Data protection can also be achieved, at least in theory, through various forms of self-regulation, in which companies and industry bodies establish codes of practice. The record of these efforts has been disappointing, with little or no evidence that the aims of the codes are regularly fulfilled. Adequacy and enforcement are the major problem with these approaches. Industry codes in many countries have tended to provide only weak protections and lack enforcement. This is currently the policy promoted by the governments of United States, Singapore, Japan, and Australia.

User-driven - With the recent development of commercially available technology-based systems, privacy protection has also moved into the hands of individual users. Users of the Internet can employ a range of programs and systems that will ensure various degrees of privacy and security of communications. Questions remain about security and trustworthiness of these systems. Recently, the European Commission evaluated some of the technologies and stated that the tools would not replace a legal framework [59].

The remedies proposed are principally safeguards for the individual that will prevent an invasion of privacy in the classical sense, i.e., abuse or disclosure of intimate personal data; but other, more or less closely related, needs for protection have become apparent. Obligations of record-keepers to inform the general public about activities concerned with the processing of data, and rights of data subjects to have data relating to them supplemented or amended, are examples. Generally speaking, there has been a tendency to broaden the traditional concept of privacy ("the right to be left alone") and to identify a more complex synthesis of interests which can perhaps more correctly be termed privacy and individual liberties.

The approaches to protection of privacy and individual liberties adopted by the various countries have some common features. Thus, it is possible to identify certain basic interests or values that are commonly considered to be elementary components of the area of protection. Some core principles found in most regulatory and legal instruments include:

- Setting limits to the collection of personal data in accordance with the objectives of the data collector and similar criteria;

- Restricting the use of data to conform with openly specified purposes;

- Creating facilities for individuals to learn of the existence and contents of data and have data corrected; and

- Identification of parties who are responsible for compliance with the relevant privacy protection rules and decisions.

Generally speaking, statutes to protect privacy and individual liberties in relation to personal data attempt to cover the successive stages of the cycle, beginning with the initial collection of data and ending with erasure or similar measures, and to ensure to the greatest possible extent individual awareness, participation, and control.

Opinions, however, vary with respect to licensing requirements and control mechanisms in the form of special supervisory bodies ("data inspection authorities"). Also, categories of sensitive data are defined differently and the means of ensuring openness and individual participation vary.

Existing traditional differences between legal systems are a cause of disparity, both with respect to legislative approaches and the detailed formulation of the regulatory framework for personal data protection. Some countries consider that the protection required for data relating to individuals may be similar in nature to the protection required for data relating to business enterprises, associations, and groups that may or may not possess legal personality. The experience of a number of countries also shows that it is difficult to define clearly the dividing line between personal and non-personal data. For example, data relating to a small company may also concern its owner or owners and provide personal information of a more or less sensitive nature. In such instances it may be advisable to extend to corporate entities the protection offered by rules relating primarily to personal data.

4.5. International Aspects of Privacy and Databases

For a number of reasons the problems of developing safeguards for the individual with respect to the handling of personal data cannot be solved exclusively at the national level. The increase in data flow across national borders and the creation of international data banks have highlighted the need for concerted national action and at the same time support arguments in favor of free flows of information that must often be balanced against requirements for data protection and for restrictions on their collection, processing, and dissemination.

One basic concern at the international level is for consensus on the fundamental principles on which protection of the individual must be based. Such a consensus would facilitate resolving problems of conflict of laws. Moreover, it could constitute a first step towards the development of more detailed, binding international agreements.

Other reasons why the regulation of the processing of personal data should be considered in an international context are:

- Principles involve concern values that many nations are anxious to uphold and see generally accepted;

- The international mobility of people, goods, and commercial and scientific activities. Commonly accepted practices with regard to the processing of data may be advantageous even where no transborder data traffic is directly involved;

- A comprehensive and broadly accepted regulatory framework may help to save costs in international data traffic; and

- Countries have a common interest in preventing the creation of locations where national regulations on data processing can easily be circumvented.

5. Review of Regulatory Responses: International Organizations

To offer but a glimpse of international regulatory environments, legislative actions, and legal complexities, brief summaries of existing efforts to deal with privacy protection of electronic health information are set forth below. It is important to remember that countries are sovereignties, each with its own executive, legislative, and judicial powers and systems. Examining the current status of how electronic health information is treated is much like shooting at many moving targets as a large number of variables are changing continuously and simultaneously.

5.1. The United Nations Guidelines for Computerized Personal Data Files

The procedures for implementing regulations concerning computerized personal data files are left to the initiative of each State, subject to the following guidelines adopted by the General Assembly on 14 December 1990 [57]:

A. Principles concerning the minimum guarantees that should be provided in national legislation

(1) Principle of lawfulness and fairness - Information about persons should not be collected or processed in unfair or unlawful ways, nor should it be used for ends contrary to the purposes and principles of the Charter of the United Nations.

(2) Principle of accuracy - Persons responsible for the compilation of files or those responsible for keeping them have an obligation to conduct regular checks on the accuracy and relevance of the data recorded and to ensure that they are kept as complete as possible in order to avoid errors of omission and that they are kept up to date regularly or when the information contained in a file is used, as long as they are being processed.

(3) Principle of the purpose-specification - The purpose which a file is to serve and its utilization in terms of that purpose should be specified, legitimate and, when it is established, receive a certain amount of publicity or be brought to the attention of the person concerned, in order to make it possible subsequently to ensure that: (a) All the personal data collected and recorded remain relevant and adequate to the purposes so specified; (b) None of the said personal data is used or disclosed, except with the consent of the person concerned, for purposes incompatible with those specified; (c) The period for which the personal data are kept does not exceed that which would enable the achievement of the purpose so specified.

(4) Principle of interested-person access - Everyone who offers proof of identity has the right to know whether information concerning him is being processed and to obtain it in an intelligible form, without undue delay or expense, and to have appropriate rectifications or erasures made in the case of unlawful, unnecessary or inaccurate entries and, when it is being communicated, addressees. Provision should be made for a remedy, if need be with the supervisory authority specified in principle 8 below. The cost of any rectification shall be borne by the person responsible for the file. It is desirable that the provisions of this principle should apply to everyone, irrespective of nationality or place of residence.

(5) Principle of non-discrimination - Subject to cases of exceptions restrictively envisaged under principle 6, data likely to give rise to unlawful or arbitrary discrimination, including information on racial or ethnic origin, color, sex life, political opinions, religious, philosophical, and other beliefs, as well as membership of an association or trade union, should not be compiled.

(6) Power to make exceptions - Departures from principles 1 to 4 may be authorized only if they are necessary to protect national security, public order, public health or morality, as well as, *inter alia*, the rights and freedoms of others, especially persons being persecuted (humanitarian clause) provided that such departures are expressly specified in a law or equivalent regulation promulgated in accordance with the internal legal system which expressly states their limits and sets forth appropriate safeguards. Exceptions to principle 5 relating to the prohibition of discrimination, in addition to being subject to the same safeguards as those prescribed for exceptions to principles 1 and 4, may be authorized only within the limits prescribed by the International Bill of Human Rights and the other relevant instruments in the field of protection of human rights and the prevention of discrimination.

(7) Principle of security - Appropriate measures should be taken to protect the files against both natural dangers, such as accidental loss or destruction and human dangers, such as unauthorized access, fraudulent misuse of data, or contamination by computer viruses.

(8) Supervision and sanctions - The law of every country shall designate the authority which, in accordance with its domestic legal system, is to be responsible for supervising observance of the principles set forth above. This authority shall offer guarantees of impartiality, independence vis-a-vis persons or agencies responsible for processing and establishing data, and technical competence. In the event of violation of the provisions of the national law implementing the aforementioned principles, criminal or other penalties should be envisaged together with the appropriate individual remedies.

(9) Transborder data flows - When the legislation of two or more countries concerned by a transborder data flow offers comparable safeguards for the protection of privacy, information should be able to circulate as freely as inside each of the territories concerned. If there are no reciprocal safeguards, limitations on such circulation may not be imposed unduly and only insofar as the protection of privacy demands.

(10) Field of application - The present principles should be made applicable, in the first instance, to all public and private computerized files as well as, by means of optional extension and subject to appropriate adjustments, to manual files. Special provision, also optional, might be made to extend all or part of the principles to files on legal persons particularly when they contain some information on individuals.

B. Application of the guidelines to personal data files kept by governmental international organizations

The present guidelines should apply to personal data files kept by governmental international organizations, subject to any adjustments required to take account of any differences that might exist between files for internal purposes such as those that concern personnel management and files for external purposes concerning third parties having relations with the organization.

Each organization should designate the authority statutorily competent to supervise the observance of these guidelines.

Humanitarian clause: a derogation from these principles may be specifically provided for when the purpose of the file is the protection of human rights and fundamental freedoms of the individual concerned or humanitarian assistance.

A similar derogation should be provided in national legislation for governmental international organizations whose headquarters agreement does not preclude the implementation of the said national legislation as well as for non-governmental international organizations to which this law is applicable.

5.2. Council of Europe's 1981 Convention for the Protection of Individuals With Regard to the Automatic Processing of Personal Data

The roots of European regulation on data protection lie significantly with the Council of Europe, rather than with the European Union. As long ago as 1950 in the Convention for the Protection of Human Rights and Fundamental Freedoms. The Convention protects the right to privacy in Article 8.1 as a "right to respect for his private and family life, his home and his correspondence". The particular protection of privacy in the use of computers did not form part of a Council of Europe regulation until 1981 when the Council of Europe Convention 108 was developed.

The object of Convention on the Protection of Individuals with regard to Automatic Processing of Personal Data of 1981 (European Treaty Series No. 108) [55], is to secure the fundamental rights and freedoms of the individual in respect of privacy in automatic processing of personal data. As much of the subsequent legislation in this area it focuses on the way in which data are gathered, the purposes for which they are gathered and the way in which they are handled and stored.

Medical data are considered within Article 6, which sets out the requirements for special safeguards in the processing of "Special Categories of Personal Data" and prohibits such processing, unless domestic law provides appropriate safeguards. Aware that medical data are increasingly processed automatically and that a harmonization of standards of protection between signatory States varies greatly in its thirty-eight Member States, the Council of Europe passed in 1981 a regulation on Automated Medical Data Banks (Recommendation No. R(81)1). That Regulation did not however gain much acceptance in the signatory states and has been superseded by Recommendation No. R (97)5 on the Protection of Medical Data, which was signed on 13 February 1997 [60].

5.3. The Organization for Economic Cooperation and Development (OECD) Guidelines Governing Privacy and Transborder Data Flows

A feature of OECD Member countries over the past two decades has been the development of laws for the protection of privacy. In the period 1973-1980 more than one-third of the OECD Member countries already had enacted one or several laws which, among other things, are intended to protect individuals against abuse of data relating to them and to give them the right of access to data with a view to checking their accuracy and appropriateness. In federal states, laws of this kind may be found both at the national and at the state or provincial level. Such laws are referred to differently in different countries. Thus, it is common practice in continental Europe to talk about "data laws" or "data protection laws" (lois sur la protection des données), whereas in English-speaking countries they are usually known as "privacy protection laws".

These laws have tended to assume different forms in different countries, and in many countries they still are in the process of being developed. The disparities in legislation may create obstacles to the free flow of information between countries. Such flows have greatly increased in recent years and are bound to continue to grow as a result of the introduction of new computer and communication technology.

The OECD decided to address the problems of diverging national legislation and in 1978 instructed a Group of Experts to develop a set of guidelines on basic rules governing the transborder flow and the protection of personal data and privacy, in order to facilitate the harmonization of national legislation. Although national laws and policies may differ, OECD Member countries have shown a common interest in protecting privacy and individual liberties, and in reconciling fundamental but competing values such as privacy and the free flow of information. It was also recognized that automatic processing and transborder flows of personal data create new forms of relationships among countries, contribute to economic and social development, but require the development of compatible rules and practices.

Determined to advance the free flow of information between Member countries and to avoid the creation of unjustified obstacles to the development of economic and social relations among Member countries, the Guidelines, adopted in 1980, are broad in nature and reflect the debate and legislative work that occurred for several years in Member countries [56]. The Guidelines apply to personal data, whether in the public or private sectors, which, because of the manner in which they are processed, or because of their nature or the context in which they are used, pose a danger to privacy and individual liberties.

Regarding the implementation of the Guidelines, the OECD recommended that Member countries should:

- Take into account in their domestic legislation the principles concerning the protection of privacy and individual liberties set forth in the Guidelines.

- Endeavor to remove or avoid creating, in the name of privacy protection, unjustified obstacles to transborder flows of personal data.

- Cooperate in the implementation of the Guidelines.

- Agree as soon as possible on specific procedures of consultation and cooperation for the application of the Guidelines.

- Consider that exceptions to the Guidelines, including those relating to national sovereignty, national security, and public policy should be as few as possible and made known to the public.

- In the particular case of Federal countries, the observance of these Guidelines may be affected by the division of powers in the Federation.

- That the Guidelines should be regarded as minimum standards, which are capable of being supplemented by additional measures for the protection of privacy and individual liberties.

The following basic principles apply to national deployment:

Collection limitation principle - There should be limits to the collection of personal data and any such data should be obtained by lawful and fair means and, where appropriate, with the knowledge or consent of the data subject.

Data quality principle - Personal data should be relevant to the purposes for which they are to be used, and, to the extent necessary for those purposes, should be accurate, complete and up-to-date.

Purpose specification principle - The purposes for which personal data are collected should be specified at the time of data collection and the subsequent use limited to the fulfillment of those purposes or such others that are not incompatible with those purposes and specified on each occasion of change of purpose.

Use limitation principle - Personal data should not be disclosed, made available, or otherwise used for purposes other than those specified in accordance with the previous principle except (a) with the consent of the data subject; or (b) by the authority of law.

Security safeguards principle - Personal data should be protected by reasonable security safeguards against such risks as loss or unauthorized access, destruction, use, modification, or disclosure of data.

Openness principle - There should be a general policy of openness about developments, practices and policies with respect to personal data. Means should be readily available of establishing the existence and nature of personal data, and the main purposes of their use, as well as the identity and usual residence of the data controller.

Individual participation principle - An individual should have the right to: (a) obtain from a data controller, or otherwise, confirmation of whether or not the data controller has data relating to him; (b) have communicated to him data relating to him within a reasonable time at a charge, if any, that is not excessive; in a reasonable manner; and in a form that is readily intelligible to him; (c) be given reasons if a request made under subparagraphs (a) and (b) is denied, and to be able to challenge such denial; and (d) to challenge data relating to him and, if the challenge is successful to have the data erased, rectified, completed, or amended.

Accountability principle - A data controller should be accountable for complying with measures that give effect to the principles stated above.

In implementing the principles, Member countries should establish legal, administrative, or other procedures or institutions for the protection of privacy and individual liberties with respect to personal data. Member countries should in particular endeavor to:

- Adopt appropriate domestic legislation;

- Encourage and support self-regulation, whether in the form of codes of conduct or otherwise;

- Provide for reasonable means for individuals to exercise their rights;

- Provide for adequate sanctions and remedies in case of failures to comply with measures that implement the principles;

- Ensure that there is no unfair discrimination against data subjects.

The following recommendations were set forth in the international application of the Guidelines:

- Member countries should take into consideration the implications for other Member countries of domestic processing and re-export of personal data.

- Member countries should take all reasonable and appropriate steps to ensure that transborder flows of personal data, including transit through a Member country, are uninterrupted and secure.

- A Member country should refrain from restricting transborder flows of personal data between itself and another Member country except where the latter does not yet substantially observe the Guidelines or where the re-export of such data would circumvent its domestic privacy legislation. A Member country may also impose restrictions with respect to certain categories of personal data for which its domestic privacy legislation includes specific regulations in view of the nature of those data and for which the other Member country provides no equivalent protection.

- Member countries should avoid developing laws, policies, and practices in the name of the protection of privacy and individual liberties that would create obstacles to transborder flows of personal data that would exceed requirements for such protection.

6. Review of Regulatory Responses: Data Protection in the European Union

The European Community is at the vanguard of the discussions of data protection and its Member States are, by far, the most advanced countries in the implementation of comprehensive regulations and legal instruments related to person-identifiable health databases. The model is based on a number of Recommendations and Directives that set a baseline common level of privacy which not only reinforces current data protection law but also extends it to establish a range of new rights.

It should be remembered that different types of legislation (Directives, Regulations, and Decisions) exist at European level. A Directive is binding on all member States to whom it is addressed and dictates "the result to be achieved" but leaves up to each Member State the choice of form and method of implementation (article 189 of the European Community). A Regulation, however, is binding in its entreaty on all Member States and has direct effect. A Decision is binding in their entirety on those to whom it is addressed. The important fact to note is that a Directive will not generally provide a citizen with a right to bring an action directly against another natural or legal person. The citizen, however, has the right to bring an action against a member State that has not implemented a Directive. For the purposes of healthcare most European Community level legislation will come in the form of a Directive.

Regarding the protection of health data, a significant aim of the Recommendation R(97)5 [60] was to provide some more detail for the medical sector to run alongside the European Union Directive 95/46/EC [33]. In accordance with this chronological development, an outline of the Directive 95/46/EC will be presented supplemented with comments on further issues raised by the Recommendation R(97)5, in particular where the Directive touches upon medical or healthcare data. For brevity, references to the Directive will be indicated by the relevant article or recital number and references to the Recommendation by the relevant principle number.

The vision in the European Union is that the concept of privacy and confidentiality must also involve the right to refuse to give access to one's own data or the right to refuse the collection of these data. From this perspective, regulations for the protection of data emphasize the necessity to recognize the citizen as a stakeholder, and information and communication technologies must offer to the individual the chance to enhance his or her choices and self-determination [30]. The vision is inspired by the idea of self-determination used for the first time by the German Constitutional Court in a judgement made in 1983. Along these lines, these provisions refer to three fundamental principles [50, 54, 55, 61]:

The principle of confidentiality - reflecting the idea that personal data are part of the identity of the individual;

The principle of autonomy - linked to the principle of consent;

The right to information - that must be an "active" right in the context of data protection. It includes the right to know what categories of information are available and the right to decide whether or not to be provided with this information.

The main difficulty with any research into the legal and ethical regulation of health informatics in Europe is that healthcare is an area that lies largely outside of the competence of the European Union as the Treaty of Rome provides only for legislation on public health. The bulk of the European legislation, in the form of Directives, which affects health information technology applications does so by virtue of its broader aim of providing consumer protection and allowing the free movement of persons, goods, services, and capital. Indeed, most of the European legal instruments in question do not specifically refer to healthcare but are nonetheless of paramount importance to the use of information technology in health practice.

6.1. Legislative Instruments

European legislative instruments have a vital role to play in creating a framework for the use of electronic records in healthcare. The most important of these instruments is the "Directive 95/46/EC of the

European Parliament and of the Council of 24 October 1995 on the Protection of Individuals with Regard to the Processing of Personal Data and on the Movement of Such Data" [33].

The objective of the Directive 95/46/EC

The Directive come into force on October 1998 and aimed at the harmonization of the laws of all European Union's Member States providing a comprehensive and coherent regulatory framework for the protection of the rights of data subjects. Legislative basis of the Directive on Data Protection is the free movement of goods, persons, services and capital as defined in Article 7a of the Treaty of Rome. The context of the Directive is therefore to assist the growth of the European market by removing barriers to the transfer of information between Member States, in situations where equal standards of data protection do not exist in each Member State. The aim of promoting data flow through data protection is stated clearly in Article 1: "Paragraph 1: In accordance with this Directive, Member States shall protect the fundamental rights and freedoms of natural persons, and in particular their right to privacy with respect to the processing of personal data. Paragraph 2: Member States shall neither restrict nor prohibit the free flow of personal data between member States for reasons connected with the protection afforded under Paragraph 1."

To what type of data and data processing does the legislation applies?

The Directive is addressed to both automatic and manual processing of all personal data of an identified or identifiable natural person. Where the data are processed manually, the Directive shall apply only where the data are "structured according to specific criteria relating to individuals" (Recital 27). Accordingly, the Directive shall not apply to situations where notes about a given individual are recorded by a professional, person, or organization, and physically maintained in a filing system that is not structured to allow recall through the use of an indexing system or a set of search and retrieval criteria, – in short, a citizen's own address book, for instance, shall not be regarded as a filing system, although the precise nature of filing systems is one which may be defined by each member State. Apart from this limitation, the scope of the Directive is very broad indeed, addressing all forms of collection, recording, storage, organization, adaptation, retrieval, consultation, transmission, dissemination, blocking, erasure, or destruction of data (Article 2b).

The key factor in deciding if data are subject to the laws developed in accordance with the Directive lies in deciding if the data identifies or make identifiable an individual. Completely anonymous data, e.g., aggregated epidemiological data, from which an individual cannot be identified will not be covered by such laws. The difficulty lies of course in defining the term "identifiable". It is not clear from the Directive what extremes of "identity cracking" a data controller should envisage, the recitals state simply that account should be taken of "means reasonably likely to be used" (Recital 26).

Who is responsible for the protection of processed data?

The individual responsible for ensuring that identifiable data are collected and stored in accordance with the legal requirements shall be the natural or legal person or persons who determine the purposes and means of the processing of the data. This person is known as the "data controller" and is responsible not only for his/her own behavior but also for that of his/her staff. In some cases it will be difficult to establish if responsibility for a breach of confidentiality lies with the controller, or if the acts of the person employed by him were beyond his/her control, in which circumstances he should be exempted from liability (Article 23.2).

In terms of medical data processing and transmission, a situation may take place where a breach of confidentiality arises not because the controller or his/her agent has failed to collect or store the data properly, but because the media used for transmitting the data between two parties allows a breach to occur. The Directive suggests that normally the controller will be regarded as the person from whom the message originates, rather than the person offering or controlling the data transmission services, which however, may still share part or all the liabilities. In terms of complex medical data storage, processing, retrieval, transmission, and use, another dimension may however be more relevant. There are applications of such systems in which they could be regarded as medical devices, to which the Medical Devices Directive (93/42/EEC) [62] may apply. In such cases the producer of the device will be strictly liable for any fault that arises. Where the system is not seen as a medical device, some or all liability for breaches of confidentiality may still rest with the producer of the storage or transmission system under product liability legislation. However, it should be noted that the Directive on liability for Defective Products (85/374/EEC) [63] is restricted to tangible and technical components that may be defective – an error on the level of man-machine interaction will in practice often lead to a shared liability between the system's provider and the system's user.

The General rules: a framework

The Directive sets up a number of key actors in data processing who have rights and duties, and seeks to regulate the relationships between them. The relationships between the players may described by the diagram below (Figure 2.), where the data controller is the player charged with the key responsibility of maintaining standards of data protection and the flows of information are governed by various rules provided by the Directive.

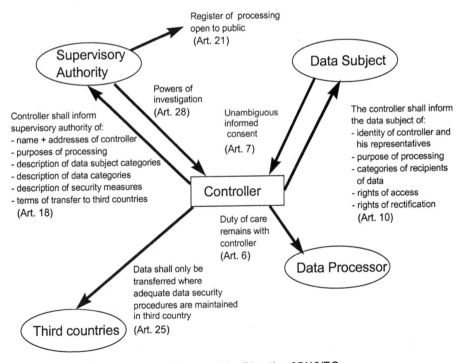

Figure 2. Core Articles of the Directive 95/46/EC

Duties of the "data controller"

The data controller has the duty to ensure that all data are processed fairly and lawfully. The Directive specifies that:

- The purposes for collection must be specified, explicit, and legitimate and that processing must only be for the purposes declared to the data subject at the time of data collection and data may not be used for other purposes later (Article 6.1 (b)). In the medical setting it should be noted that further processing for scientific research purposes might be acceptable even if not originally declared to the data subject as long as appropriate care to ensure confidentiality is taken (Recital 34).

- Data collected must be adequate, relevant and not excessive for the purposes stated (Article 6.1(c)),

- Data collected must be accurate and kept up to date where that is relevant (Article 6.1(d))

- Data must not be stored in an identifiable form for longer than necessary for the completion of the specified purpose (Article 6.1(e)).

- The data controller is also duty bound to ensure that data are protected against accidental or unlawful destruction, loss, alteration or unauthorized access by use of appropriate organizational and technical security measures (Article 17).

Whether or not the security measures used are adequate shall be judged on the basis of a balance of the current state of the art and the costs of implementing appropriate security measures, as well as the nature of the data and the processing. Where the data are particular sensitive, such as medical- and health-related data, the security standards must be high. While the Directive speaks of standards of security in blanket terms, the Recommendation R(97)5 stresses the elements of integrity and availability of data specifically [60]. It may be argued, therefore, that in designing a security system for medical data due reference must be made to the three elements traditionally considered to be part of data protection: reliability, security, and privacy and their respective protective policies, tools, and actions addressing issues of physical data protection, data integrity, data access, and data confidentiality.

Rights of the data subject

The data subject has the right to give or withhold his/her consent to the processing of his/her data, and must give that consent unambiguously (Article 7). In accordance with other legal definitions of consent the Directive specifies that the consent must be given freely and on the basis of adequate information about the purposes of collection and the eventual recipients of the information (Articles 10 and 11). The data subject must also be given access to information about the nature of data held about him/her and the purpose or purposes for which data are processed. Such access must be given at reasonable intervals and without undue delay or expense to the data subject (Article 12).

The rights of the data subject may be limited or circumvented for particular reasons. First among these are the vital interest of the data subject or some greater public interest (Article 7). Thus it might be acceptable to argue that for the welfare or emergency health reasons of the very data subject or of another person or persons, the patient's consent need not be sought before processing, nor should he/she be given access to his/her data. Justifications for processing without the consent of the data subject will also arise where the data are processed in performance of a contract to which the data subject is party, or where a legal duty to process exists. The Directive itself is, of course, limited to areas of EU competence and, accordingly, a Member State may choose to vary or abandon data protection principles in the interests of public security, defense and criminal law issues if it chooses to do so.

Special provision for medical data

In handling medical data all the rights and duties outlined above must be observed. Medical data must satisfy the same quality standards laid down in Article 7 as other categories of data and the patient has the

59

same rights to be informed about his/her data handling as any other data subject and the same duties exist for the data controller.

However, in terms of the Directive, all processing of medical data is done within the context of an exception to the general rule prohibiting the collection and processing of "data revealing racial or ethnic origin, political opinions, religious or philosophical beliefs, trade-union membership, and the processing of data concerning health or sex life" (Article 8.1). The general prohibition of Article 8.1 therefore does not apply to medical and health-related data are collected and processed for the purposes of preventative medicine, medical diagnosis, the provision of care or treatment, or the management of healthcare services. This generally wide exception may be used to justify the collection of most health-related data. Accordingly, health-related data may be gathered and processed where the requirements of data quality have been met and where the appropriate level of security protection has been implemented.

As already indicated, generally it is required that the patient has given his/her consent to the collection and processing of the data, however, this requirement may be overridden where the data subject is physically or legally incapable of giving his/her consent, when processing is necessary to protect the vital interests of the data subject or another person, or when public interests dictates that the requirement of consent is not relevant in given set of circumstances.

The Directive further stipulates that the data must be processed only by a health professional subject, under national law or nationally competent bodies, and bound to an obligation of professional secrecy (Article 8.3). Where the data are handled by someone who is not a health professional, such as a clerk or secretary, an equivalent obligation of secrecy must exist, one would expect to find clauses for summary dismissal for inappropriate breach of confidentiality in the employment contracts of all such staff.

While the Directive provides for clinicians, the organizations for whom they work, and network providers to protect the security and confidentiality of patient identifiable information, another Directive on the processing of personal data and the protection of privacy in the telecommunications sector (Directive 97/66/EC), usually referred to as the Telecommunications Directive [58], goes somewhat further than the Directive 95/46/EC by providing protection to data subjects whether those subjects be natural persons (i.e., individuals, as in the Directive 95/46/EC) or legal persons, such as corporations and public authorities, which are not covered by the Directive 95/46/EC. Furthermore, the Telecommunications Directive provides for a specific duty incumbent upon telecommunications service providers to protect the privacy of data subjects and applies to data that are processed pursuant to the provision of telecommunications services over public networks. The Council of Europe's "Recommendation on the Protection of Medical Data No. R(97)5" provides further guidance on appropriate security measures for healthcare providers [60].

6.2. Interactive Communications

Privacy issues related to the development of the Internet raised great concern in the European Union. A growing amount of services are available to the Internet user, from shopping online to participating in fora with people all around the world. Frequently, companies attract users and distinguish themselves from others by offering personalized or free services. Personalization of the services is dependent upon utilization of personal user data, which companies try to obtain using different sources, such as encouraging the provision of such data by the users themselves in the framework of loyalty programs, free gifts or services, collection from public available sources, etc.

User profiles are valuable for the companies who want to target a consumer and have also an economic value in themselves, as they are often sold or hired to others. In this context, it becomes difficult for the average user to remain anonymous while being on the Internet. The combination of these developing capabilities brings with it new risks for the privacy of the Internet user, especially when data are concentrated in the hands of one or a limited number of controllers.

When these controllers make use of data mining technologies they have the technical possibility not only of processing and reorganizing the data but also to uncover new links and characteristics related to the data subject, who is usually not aware of this possibility and does not expect such a processing. Such risks also arise from the fact that some data are preserved online for a very long period of time; for instance, the messages posted to newsgroups and mailing lists are often kept several years and can be consulted using reverse search tools. Such availability of personal data enables unexpected secondary use of those data, which is often incompatible with the purpose for which the data were originally collected.

Guidelines and recommendations regarding an integrated approach to online data protection were developed by a Working Party of the EU Advisory Body on Data Protection and Privacy of the European Commission's Internal Market Directorate General and approved on November 2000 [64]. They include actions and regulatory intervention directed to:

Raising the awareness of the Internet user - to ensure that adequate means are put into place in order to ensure that the user gets all the information he/she needs to make an informed choice. Several actors have a role to play in the provision of this information to the user: (a) The controller collecting personal data online has to give all necessary information to the data subject. This information, mentioned in article 10 of Directive 95/46/EC, shall be given in all cases at the occasion of the collection of data. Although having a privacy policy posted on the website is a good way of providing general information to the public, it is necessary to provide information to the data subject from which the data are being collected, in a simple and accessible way each time that data are collected; (b) Where the data controller is a private company, the compliance with these rules is important not only in legal terms but also out of commercial self-interest, as the trust and confidence of individuals will increase and might have an impact in the involvement of the individual with the company. As regards the development of e-commerce, for instance, it is being observed that users are reluctant to engage in electronic transactions if they fear that their personal data will not be correctly protected and secured; (c) Where the controller is a public authority, the compliance with the data protection rules is a key element as the behavior of such authority should be an example for the public in general. For instance, public authorities implementing e-government activities should build in privacy as one of the cornerstones of the system of exchange of data. Besides, even when they do not play a role of data controller, the responsibility of these authorities lies in the field of general education and information of the public; (d) Privacy-supporting associations and advocates have traditionally been performing such public awareness activities, in a way that has sometimes led to significant improvements as regards the privacy compliance of Internet products; (e) Consumer associations are also increasingly getting involved and interested in the privacy aspects of consumer activities. Such a role can be particularly positive, as it does not limit itself to the provision of information but also extends to the representation of consumers in their relation with companies or public authorities. Such associations can, for instance, monitor the compliance of Internet Service Providers (ISPs) with the laws, or inform public authorities about the complaints they receive about a specific website or Internet company. Professional associations can also have a positive influence, informing new actors about their legal obligations.

Applying existing legislation in a coherent and coordinated way - online data protection can be sufficiently guaranteed only if the existent legal framework is complied with. Considering the international character of the network, it is essential that data controllers can rely on a coherent and coordinated interpretation and application of the European data protection rules. This is important not only for data subjects and controllers inside the EU but also for those outside the Union that also have to take this legal framework into consideration, in particular when they collect personal data using means located inside the Union. The Working Party identified some lacunae or controversial issues in the existing legislation and issued documents providing for common interpretation and possible solutions. Special attention has been paid to the revision of the Directive 97/66/EC, which has brought with it some significant improvements in the terminology used. It was emphasized that interpretation and application of the legislation is not only the task of public authorities; the private sector can provide fruitful contribution by investing in the development of self-regulation or codes of conduct addressing more specific issues raised in a particular sector.

Developing and using privacy-compliant, privacy-friendly, and privacy-enhancing technologies - the processing of personal data on the Internet very much depends on the technical configuration of the hardware and software as well as on the protocols and technical standards used for the transmission of information. It is therefore especially important to take into account privacy requirements at the earliest stage of developing all these tools; e.g., a browser should not transmit more information than necessary to establish a connection to a website. While new technologies are traditionally considered as a threat to privacy, it should be stressed that they also represent a useful tool in terms of safeguarding privacy. Some of the existing technologies can be used to improve the transparency and the friendliness of the information provided to the data subject by giving users simple and accessible information at the moment of collection of personal data. They can be a useful tool to simplify the exercise of the rights of the data subjects by allowing a direct access online to the personal data of the individual or giving the possibility to oppose the processing. Those involved in the design and development of these technical tools are encouraged to consult the national Data Protection Authorities about the existing data protection legal requirements. Moreover, in order to make clear to the general public which products are privacy-compliant, it would be useful to put in place a system of certification marks that would allow an easy recognition of those products that comply with the data protection requirements.

Building trusted mechanisms for control and feedback - online data protection can be effective only if adequate means are in place to monitor and evaluate the compliance with the legal framework and technical requirements explained above. For that purpose, even if data protection authorities are in charge of the control of enforcement in the first place, other actors are taking steps in the direction of self-monitoring, as they have realized the impact of their privacy policy on the behavior of the consumers towards them. Data protection authorities can contribute to the development and proper functioning of such self-monitoring systems by providing guidance, e.g., the checklists for self-evaluation agreed at European level. Furthermore, a "seal of approval" could be granted with a view of helping the consumer get a trustworthy indication of the compliance of a data processing with EU Data protection legislation.

6.3. Transborder Data Flow

In June 2001 the European Commission adopted a Decision [65] setting out standard contractual clauses ensuring adequate safeguards for personal data transferred from the EU to countries outside the Union. The Decision obliges Member States to recognize that companies or organizations using such standard clauses in contracts concerning personal data transfers to countries outside the EU are offering "adequate protection" to the data.

The Decision is aligned with the Data Protection Directive (95/46/EC) which requires all personal data transferred to countries outside the Union to benefit from protection. Application of those standard contractual clauses will be voluntary, but will offer companies and organizations a straightforward means of complying with their obligation to ensure "adequate protection" for personal data transferred to countries outside the EU which have not been recognized by the Commission as providing adequate protection for such data.

So far, only Switzerland, Hungary and the United States "Safe Harbor" arrangement have been recognized as providing adequate protection [65,66].

According to the Decision, the lawfulness of the transfer under national law remains entirely subject to the conditions of the national legislation implementing the provisions of the Directive 95/46/EC. Should a transfer by means of the standard contractual clauses approved by the Commission not fulfil the conditions set up in the national law as regards these aspects, the intended transfer to third countries could not take place. In particular, if a disclosure of data to a third party recipient inside a Member State of the controller would not be lawful, the mere circumstance that the recipient may be situated in a third country does not change this legal evaluation.

By definition, the recipient of the personal data transferred by means of the standard contractual clauses approved by the Commission is established in a country where there is no adequate protection for the privacy of individuals. The standard contractual clauses would allow the transfer, provided that the "data importer" effectively complies with them. If that was not the case, the standard contractual clauses would no longer fulfil their role of providing sufficient safeguards and, therefore, a suspension or prohibition of the transfer could take place.

The "data importer" must agree and warrant to process the personal data received from the Community in accordance with certain processing conditions that allow the "data importer" to prove that enough safeguards within the meaning of Article 26 (2) of the Directive 95/46/EC were implemented, in order to guarantee a minimum level of protection, the purpose limitation principle, restrictions on onward transfers and the data importer's undertaking of providing the data subjects with the rights of access, rectification, deletion, and objection.

It was recommended that joint and severe liability, applied to the "data exporter" and the "data importer", regarding any damages resulting from the violation of the standard contractual clauses is the only way to address, in an efficient and realistic manner, the serious difficulties that the contractual solution poses for the enforcement of individuals' rights and proper compensation for damages.

6.4. Status of Implementation of Directive 95/45/EC

As already noted, a Directive requires transposition into national law in order to have effect. The EU has regularly carried out studies concerning the problems of harmonization of national legislation within the Community, in relation to transborder data flows and possible distortions of competition, the problems of data security and confidentiality, and the nature of data flows. The Guidelines should not be applied in a mechanical way irrespective of the kind of data and processing activities involved.

The framework provided by the basic principles Guidelines permits Member countries to exercise their discretion with respect to the degree of stringency with which the Guidelines are to be implemented, and with respect to the scope of the measures to be taken. Member countries might apply the Guidelines differentially to different kinds of personal data. There may be differences in the permissible frequency of inspection, in ways of balancing competing interests such as the confidentiality of medical records versus the individual's right to inspect data relating to him, and so forth. Member countries are implicitly encouraged to consider the need to adapt rules and practices for the processing of data to the particular circumstances which may arise when foreign data and data on non-nationals are involved. The implementation status of the Directive 95/46/EC in the Member States of the European Union is summarized in Table 1.

Table 1. Implementation Status of the Directive 95/46/EC In the European Union Member States as of July 2000

Member State	State of Legislative Procedure	Next Steps
Austria	Directive implemented by the Data Protection Act 2000. Bundesgesetz über den Schutz personenbezogener Daten (Datenschutzgesetz 2000 . DSG-2000) vom 17.08.1999 Entry into force: 1.01.2000. Adopted ordinances: Verordnung des Bundeskanzlers über den angemessenen Datenschutz in Drittstaaten (Datenschutzangemessenheits-Verordnung - DSAV), Federal Law Gazette II Nr. 521/1999, about countries with adequate DP legislation (Switzerland and Hungary); Verordnung des Bundeskanzlers über das bei der Datenschutzkommission eingerichtete Datenverarbeitungsregister (Datenverarbeitungsregister-Verordnung 2000 - DVRV), Federal Law Gazette II Nr. 520/1999, about the registration procedure; and Verordnung des Bundeskanzlers über Standard- und Musteranwendungen nach dem Datenschutzgesetz 2000 (Standard- und Muster-Verordnung 2000 - StMV), Federal Law Gazette II Nr. 201/2000, about exceptions from notification.	

Belgium	Implementation Law passed by Parliament on 11.12.1998 (O.J. 03.02.1999). Consolidated text of the Belgian law of December 8, 1992, on Privacy Protection in relation to the Processing of Personal Data as modified by the law of December 11, 1998. In December 1999 a public consultation of the draft of the secondary legislation was launched via the Internet.	Secondary legislation to be adopted.
Denmark	Parliament passed the Act. No. 429 of 31.05.2000 on processing of personal data on 26.05.2000. 'The Act on Processing of Personal Data (Act No. 429) of 31 May 2000' Entry into force: 01.07.2000.	
Finland	The Finnish Personal Data Act (523/1999) was given on 22.4.1999 Entry into force: 01.06.1999.	
France	The Government consulted the data protection authority (La Commission nationale de l'informatique et des libertés) on the pre-draft of the bill in July 2000.	Parliamentary discussions likely.
Germany	Draft Bill adopted by Federal Government on 14.06.2000 and presented to the Parliamentary bodies. The Federal Data Protection Act will cover Federal public authorities as well as private sector. Six Länder (Brandenburg, Baden-Württemberg, Bayern, Hessen, Nordrhein-Westfalen, Schleswig-Holstein) adopted new DPLs pursuant to the Directive. These acts apply to the public sector of the respective Länder. Brandenburg: Gesetz zum Schutz personenbezogener Daten im Land Brandenburg (Brandenburgisches Datenschutzgesetz – bgDSG) in der Fassung der Bekanntmachung vom 9. März 1999. Baden-Württemberg: Gesetz zum Schutz personenbezogener Daten (Landesdatenschutzgesetz - LDSG) vom 27. Mai 1991, zuletzt geändert durch Artikel 1 des Gesetzes zur Änderung des Landesdatenschutz-gesetzes und anderer Gesetze vom 23. Mai 2000. Bayern: Bayerisches Datenschutzgesetz (BayDSG) vom 23. Juli 1993, zuletzt geändert durch Gesetz zur Änderung des Bayerischen Datenschutzgesetzes vom 25.10.2000 (Inkrafttreten zum 1.1.2001). Nordrhein-Westfalen: Gesetz zum Schutz personenbezogener Daten (Datenschutzgesetz Nordrhein-Westfalen-DSG NRW-) in der Fassung der Bekanntmachung vom 9. Juni 2000.	The Bundesrat presented an opinion on 29.9.2000 (BR-Drs. 461/00 (Beschluss). First Reading by the Deutscher Bundestag on 27.10.2000.

	Hessen: Hessisches Datenschutzgesetz (HDSG) in der Fassung vom 7. Januar 1999. Schleswig-Holstein: Schleswig-Holsteinisches Gesetz zum Schutz personenbezogener Informationen vom 9. Februar 2000.	
Greece	Implementation Law 2472 adopted: 10.04. 1997. Protection of individuals with regard to the processing of personal data Entry into force: 10 4.1997.	
Ireland	Draft bill considered by the Government in July 1998 in view of presenting it to Parliament.	Bill to be approved by the Government and submitted to Parliament
Italy	Protection of individuals and other subjects with regard to the processing of personal data Act no. 675 of 31.12.1996. Entry into force: 8.5.2000. Additional legal acts previewed by Act no. 676 of 31.12.1996 (in particular, the Legislative Decrees no. 123 of 09.05.97, no. 255 of 28.07.97, no. 135 of 08.05.98, no. 171 of 13.05.98, no. 389 of 06.11.98, no. 51 of 26.02.99, no. 135 of 11.05.99, no. 281and no. 282 of 30.07.99 ; the Presidential decrees no. 501 of 31.03.98, no. 318 of 28.07.99).	Parliamentary discussion about the renew of the delegation to the Government to complete Law 675.
Luxembourg	A new DPL was submitted to Parliament beginning October 2000.	
The Netherlands	DPL approved by the Senate on 06.07.2000 (O.J. 302/2000). Personal Data Protection Act (Wet bescherming persoonsgegevens), Act of 6 July 2000. Estimated entry into force: Spring 2001.	Secondary legislation to be adopted.
Portugal	Directive implemented by Law 67/98 of 26.10.1998. "Lei da protecção de dados pessoais'" Entry into force: 27.10.1998.	
Spain	Implementation law adopted 13.12.1999 Ley Orgánica 15/1999, de 13 de diciembre de Protección de Datos de Carácter Personal. ("B.O.E." núm. 298, de 14 de diciembre de 1999). Entry into force: 14.01.2000.	
Sweden	Directive implemented by SFS 1998:204 of 29.4.98 and regulation SFS 1998:1191 of 03.09.98. Entry into force: 24.10.1998.	
United Kingdom	Royal Assent given to Data Protection Act 1998 on 16.07.1998. Subordinate legislation passed on 17.02.2000. Entry into force: 01.03. 2000.	

7. Review of Regulatory Responses: National Initiatives in the European Union

7.1. Austria

The Austrian Constitution does not explicitly recognize the right of privacy but some sections of the data protection law (Datenschutzgesetz), enacted in 2000, have constitutional rank [67, 68]. The law concerns persons and legal entities. Most important of these is the section that reads: "Everybody has the right of secrecy of his personal data, as far as he has an interest worthy of protection, particularly regarding respect for his private and family life." Other sections grant the fundamental constitutional rights of access to personal data processed with support of automation, as well as rights to have any incorrect data corrected, and illegally obtained or processed data deleted.

The Datenschutzgesetz is enforced by the Data Protection Commission. Anybody who processes personal data has to notify or register with the Commission (Datenverarbeitungsregister). Individual rights can be asserted in the courts if the processor is not a public authority, or at the commission in all other cases. Appeals against decisions of the data protection commission can be made at the administrative court (Verwaltungsgerichtshof) or the constitutional court (Verfassungsgerichtshof). The Auskunftspflichtgesetz is a Freedom of Information law that obliges federal authorities to answer questions regarding their areas of responsibility. However, it does not permit citizens to access documents, just to receive answers from the government on the content of information. The nine Austrian Provinces have laws that place similar obligations on their authorities.

The national telecommunication law contains special data protection provisions for telecommunication systems; particularly problems like phone directories, unsolicited calls, or ISDN calling line identification. The nine Austrian Provinces have laws that place similar obligations on their authorities. Austria is a member of the Council of Europe and has signed and ratified the Convention for the Protection of

Individuals with Regard to Automatic Processing of Personal Data. Austria signed and ratified the European Convention for the Protection of Human Rights and Fundamental Freedoms and adopted the Organization for Economic Cooperation and Development Guidelines on the Protection of Privacy and Transborder Flows of Personal Data.

7.2. Belgium

The Belgian Constitution recognizes the right of privacy and private communications [69]. Article 22 states: "Everyone has the right to the respect of his private and family life, except in the cases and conditions determined by law." Article 22 was added to the Belgian Constitution in 1994. Prior to the constitutional amendment, the Cour de Cassation ruled that Article 8 of the European Convention applied directly to the law and prohibited government infringement on the private life of individuals.

A Data Protection Act of 1992 applies to automatic processing of personal data and to manual files. It requires that government agencies and private entities register their databases. There are limits on use and disclosure. Individuals have a right to access and correct their data. An amendment to make it consistent with the EU Directive is pending [70].

The Commission de la Protection de la Vie Privée oversees the law. The Commission investigates complaints, issues opinions and maintains the registry of personal files. Surveillance of communications is regulated under a 1994 law [71]. The law was amended in 1997 to remove restrictions on encryption. Belgium is a member of the Organization for Economic Cooperation and Development and has adopted the OECD Guidelines on the Protection of Privacy and Transborder Flows of Personal Data.

7.3. Denmark

The Danish Constitution of 1953 contains two provisions that have some relevance for privacy and data protection. Section 71 provides for the inviolability of personal liberty and Section 72 states: "The dwelling shall be inviolable. House searching, seizure, and examination of letters and other papers as well as any breach of the secrecy to be observed in postal, telegraph, and telephone matters shall take place only under a judicial order unless particular exception is warranted by Statute." [72]. The European Convention on Human Rights was formally incorporated into Danish law in 1992.

The central rules on data protection in Denmark are found in two Acts: the Private Registers Act of 1978 governs the private sector [73] while the Public Authorities Registers Act of 1978 governs the public sector [74]. The Private Registers Act regulates the registration and further processing of data on natural persons and on legal persons, such as private corporations. A bill for a new Data Protection Act to replace the above two Acts was approved by the Parliament in 1998 [74]. The main purpose of the new legislation is to implement the requirements of the European Community Directive on data protection. Accordingly, the new legislation follows closely the Directive. Another piece of legislation with rules relating to privacy and data protection in health is the Access to Health Information Act of 1993.

An independent agency, the Data Protection Agency (Registertilsynet), enforces the Act [76]. The agency supervises registries established by public authorities and private enterprises in Denmark. It ensures that the conditions for registration, disclosure, and storage of data on individuals, and to a certain extent also on private enterprises, are complied with. It mainly deals with specific cases on the basis of inquiries from public authorities or private individuals, or cases taken up by the agency on its own initiative.

Denmark is a member of the Council of Europe and has signed the Convention for the Protection of Individuals with Regard to Automatic Processing of Personal Data and has signed and ratified the European Convention for the Protection of Human Rights and Fundamental Freedoms. Denmark is a member of the Organization for Economic Cooperation and Development and has adopted the OECD Guidelines on the Protection of Privacy and Transborder Flows of Personal Data.

7.4.   Finland

Finland is a country that has traditionally adhered to the Nordic tradition of open access to government files. In fact, the world's first data protection act dates back as far as 1776 Riksdag's (Swedish Parliament) "Access to Public Records Act." This Act also applied to Finland, then a Swedish-governed territory. Although the 1776 Act was more of a "freedom of information act" in that the public was allowed to scrutinize public records for accuracy, it also served the purpose of ensuring that all government-held information was, in fact, required for legitimate purposes [77].

Section 10 of The Constitution of Finland states: "Everyone's private life, honor and the sanctity of the home are guaranteed. More detailed provisions on the protection of personal data are laid down by an Act. The secrecy of correspondence, telephony and other confidential communications is inviolable. Measures encroaching on the sanctity of the home, and which are necessary for the purpose of guaranteeing basic rights and liberties or for the investigation of crime, may be laid down by an Act. In addition, provisions concerning limitations of the secrecy of communications which are necessary in the investigation of crimes that jeopardize the security of the individual or society or the sanctity of the home, at trials and security checks, as well as during the deprivation of liberty may be laid down by an Act." In Section 12 it is indicated that: "Documents and recordings in the possession of the authorities are public, unless their publication has for compelling reasons been specifically restricted by an Act. Everyone has the right of access to public documents and recordings." [78].

Finland enacted its Personal Data File Act in 1987 and it became law in 1988 [79]. The Personal Data File Act applies to the public and private sectors as well as manual and automated files. There is a registration requirement for systems containing personal data. The data user must notify the Data Protection Ombudsman (DPO) of the establishment where the personal data file is maintained. The requirements and detail of this notification are dependent on the sensitivity of the data. If the information is not very sensitive, only basic information must be provided to the DPO. For more sensitive information such as credit data and data used and manipulated by third party data service organizations, the rules for notification are stricter. The DPO enforces the Act and receives complaints. A Data Protection Board resolves disputes and hears appeals of decisions rendered by the DPO. The Finnish government has enacted special ordinances that apply to particular personal data systems. These include those operated by the police such as criminal information systems, the national health service, passport systems, population registers, farm registers, and the agency responsible for motor vehicle registration [80].

Finland is a member of the Council of Europe and has signed and ratified the Convention for the Protection of Individuals with Regard to Automatic Processing of Personal Data and signed and ratified the European Convention for the Protection of Human Rights and Fundamental Freedoms. Finland is a member of the Organization for Economic Cooperation and Development and has adopted the OECD Guidelines on the Protection of Privacy and Transborder Flows of Personal Data.

7.5.   France

The right of privacy is not explicitly protected in the French Constitution of 1792. The tort of privacy was first recognized in France as far back as 1858 [81] and the Constitutional Court ruled, in 1994, that the right of privacy was implicit in the Constitution. A Data Protection Act was enacted in 1978 and covers personal information held by government agencies and private entities [82]. There are additional specific laws for administrative documents [83] and archives [84].

There are also protections incorporated in the Civil Code and Penal Code. Anyone wishing to process personal data must register and obtain permission in cases relating to processing by public bodies and for medical research. Individuals must be informed of the reasons for collection of information and may object to its processing. Individuals have rights to access and to demand corrections. Fines and imprisonment can be imposed for violations. The law was amended to make it consistent with the European Union Directive. The Commission Nationale de l'Informatique et des Libertés (CNIL) is an independent agency that enforces the Data Protection Act and other related laws.

The Commission takes complaints, issues rulings, sets rules, conducts audits, issues reports, and maintains a website [85].

France is a member of the Council of Europe and has signed and ratified the Convention for the Protection of Individuals with Regard to Automatic Processing of Personal Data and signed and ratified the European Convention for the Protection of Human Rights and Fundamental Freedoms. It is a member of the Organization for Economic Cooperation and Development and has adopted the OECD Guidelines on the Protection of Privacy and Transborder Flows of Personal Data.

7.6.   Germany

There is no specific data-related right of privacy in Germany's constitution. Attempts to introduce such a right were discussed after the German Reunification when the constitution was revised but the proposal was successfully opposed by the conservative political majority. In 1983, the Federal Constitutional Court, in a case against a government census law, acknowledged formally an individual's "right of informational self-determination" that can, however, be limited by "predominant public interest." Although there is no constitutional right of privacy or data-protection, the court decision was based on the "right of informational self-determination" directly from Article 2 of the German Constitution that declares protective personal rights (Persönlichkeitsrechte) [86].

The first Data Protection Law was passed in the State (Land) of Hessen in 1970 and it was the first data protection law worldwide. In 1977, a Federal Data Protection Act (Bundesdatenschutzgesetz) followed, which was reviewed in 1990 [87]. As every other legal matter in Germany the subject of data protection is demarcated in a twofold manner in that there are public law and private law on the one hand and Federal and States (Länder) regulations on the other hand. A further particularity of German data protection law lies in the fact that in addition to the Federal Data Protection Act, which is serving as an omnibus law, there are numerous so-called sector-specific provisions. All these rules are granting the data subject a variety of possibilities aiming at the respect of his/her individual data protection rights. The general purpose of this law is "to protect the individual against violations of his personal right by handling person-related data." The law covers collection, processing, and use of personal data collected by public federal and State authorities, as long as there is no State regulation, and of non-public offices, as long as they process and use data for commercial or professional aims.

Changes to the law to make it consistent with the European Union Directive are being debated and will likely be enacted following the election. All of the sixteen Länder (Baden-Württemberg, Bayern, Berlin, Brandenburg, Bremen, Hamburg, Hessen, Mecklenburg-Vorpommern, Niedersachsen, Nordrhein-Westfalen, Rheinland-Pfalz, Saarland, Sachsen, Sachsen-Anhalt, Schleswig-Holstein, and Thüringen) have specific data protection regulations that cover the public sector, but only six (Brandenburg, Baden-Württemberg, Bayern, Hessen, Nordrhein-Westfalen, and Schleswig-Holstein) have adopted new data protection laws aligned to the EU Directive 95/46/EC.

Public and private sector organizations must on request provide the citizen with details of the data they hold according to Sections 19 and 34 of the Federal Data Protection Act. Section 26 requires the Federal Data Protection Commissioner (Bundesbeauftragter für den Datenschutz) to keep a register of automated databanks containing personal information, which the public may consult. The Federal Data Protection Commission is responsible for supervision of the Data Protection Act [88]. The office of the Commissioner prepares an annual plan for its activities regarding supervision, investigation and auditing. It is free to set its own priorities and to create its own agenda, which is enabling it to be more responsive to current affairs.

The several units of the Commissioner's office carry out investigations of various types of information systems, based upon citizens' complaints or a suspicion that a particular area requires detailed examination. Systematic audits are planned over a several-year period, thus increasing the scope and range of data protection activities. In case infringements of the Federal Data Protection Act or of other data protection provisions or other irregularities in the processing or use of personal data are uncovered, the Commissioner will lodge a complaint. In the case of the federal administration he does so with the competent supreme federal authority and he requests a statement by a date which he determines.

The right of notification (Section 33) is an important means to answer the question of who is processing which data of a person. Furthermore there are the data subject's rights to correction, erasure and blocking of data (Sections 20 and 35) and the possibility to exercise the right of objection *vis-à-vis* the controller of the data file to the use or communication of data for purposes of advertising or of market or opinion research (Section 28). The law provides compensation by public and private bodies and regards certain misbehaviors on the controller's side as administrative or even criminal offenses. There is a statutory prescription of the appointment – under certain circumstances – of a data protection officer for private bodies (Section 36). There are also commissions in each of the Länder who enforce the local data protection acts [89].

The Telecommunications Carriers Data Protection Ordinance of 1996 protects privacy of telecommunications information [90] and the Information and Communication Services (Multimedia) Act of 1997 sets protections for information used in computer networks [91] and also sets out the legal requirements for digital signatures.

It is to be noted that the European Data Protection Directive 95/46/EC from 24 October 1995 is, at present, not yet implemented into German law. However, the bulk of the provisions of sections 21 to 26 of the Federal Data Protection Act will most certainly remain unchanged in substance. And the minor changes envisaged will altogether lead to an improvement of the Commissioner's powers. Germany is a member of the Council of Europe and has signed and ratified the Convention for the Protection of Individuals with Regard to Automatic Processing of Personal Data. It has signed and ratified the European Convention for the Protection of Human Rights and Fundamental Freedoms. It is a member of the Organization for Economic Cooperation and Development and has adopted the OECD Guidelines on the Protection of Privacy and Transborder Flows of Personal Data.

7.7. Greece

The Constitution of Greece recognizes the rights of privacy and secrecy of communications. Article 9 states: "(1) Each man's home is inviolable. A person's personal and family life is inviolable. No house searches shall be made except when and as the law directs, and always in the presence of representatives of the judicial authorities. (2) Offenders against the foregoing provision shall be punished for forced entry into a private house and abuse of power, and shall be obliged to indemnify in full the injured party as the law provides." Article 19 states: "The privacy of correspondence and any other form of communication is absolutely inviolable. The law shall determine the guarantees under which the judicial authority is released from the obligation to observe the above-mentioned right, for reasons of national security or for the investigation of particularly serious crimes" [92].

The Law on the Protection of Individuals with regard to the Processing of Personal Data was approved in 1997 [93]. Greece was the last member of the European Union to adopt a data protection law and its law was written to apply the EU Directive into Greek law. The Protection of Personal Data Authority is an independent public authority set up under the law. Its mission is to supervise the implementation of the law and the other rulings pertaining to the protection of individuals against the processing of personal data. It also exercises other powers delegated to it from time to time.

Greece is a member of the Council of Europe and has signed and ratified the Convention for the Protection of Individuals with Regard to Automatic Processing of Personal Data and signed and ratified the European Convention for the Protection of Human Rights and Fundamental Freedoms. Greece is a member of the Organization for Economic Cooperation and Development and has adopted the OECD Guidelines on the Protection of Privacy and Transborder Flows of Personal Data.

7.8. Ireland

While Irish law differs from U.K. law insofar as the Irish Constitution [94] recognizes a right to privacy, particularly in the context of communications, there was a need for specific legislative action in the field of privacy rights in relation to information gathering, retention, and use. The 1981 Strasbourg Convention was implemented in the form of the Irish Data Protection Act of 1988 [95].

The High and Supreme Courts have also ruled that privacy is protected under Article 40.3.1 ("The State guarantees in its laws to respect, and, as far as practicable, by its laws to defend and vindicate the personal rights of the citizen.") and other provisions [96]. The nature of the right to privacy is such that it must ensure the dignity and freedom of the individual in a democratic society. This cannot be ensured if his/her private communications, whether written or telephonic, are deliberately and unjustifiably interfered with.

The Data Protection Act of 1988 covers both the private and public sectors and came into effect as from 19 April 1989. It is essential to note that the legislation relates to personal data only. The legislation provides that computer users should observe a number of provisions - data protection principles – when the user is the controller of a computerized file. Data subjects may have their personal information deleted if the personal data are held for direct marketing purposes. Once the subject makes a request to have the information deleted for these purposes, the information must be deleted within forty days. Data subjects have the power to determine whether their personal data may be held by another organization or person and data subjects have the right to demand copies of their personal data files held by a data controller. The data subject must first provide notice to the data controller of the request. Additionally, the subject may be asked to pay a small fee, which is explicitly kept low by the Act, for the request to be filled. The data protection principles apply regardless of whether the controller or gatherer of personal data is registered. Subsequent unauthorized disclosure is also covered under the Act. Data held in manual formats are not covered by the Act.

The Act is enforced by the Data Protection Commissioner [97]. These obligations are applicable regardless of whether the computer user – data controller or data processor – is obliged to register with the Data Protection Commissioner, the statutory body charged with enforcing the Act. The Data Protection Commissioners regulates the collection, processing, keeping, use and disclosure of personal information that is processed automatically. Individuals have a right to access and correct incorrect information. Information can be used only for specified and lawful purposes. Additional protections can be ordered for sensitive data. Criminal penalties can be imposed for violations. There are broad exemptions for national security, tax, and criminal purposes. A draft bill is currently being reviewed by the Attorney General that would revise the Act to make it consistent with the European Union Directive.

The Commissioner can investigate complaints, prosecute offenders, sponsor codes of practice, and supervise the registration process. The computer user, whether he is a data controller or a data processor, must be registered with the Ireland Data Protection Commissioner. Failure to register without reasonable excuse is a crime for which the Commissioner may prosecute. The Data Protection Commissioner has broad authority and power to enforcement of the Act. Although the Commission is the acting prosecutor, the Commissioner is not given the power to award any damages or compensation for a violation of the Act. Any legal claim for damages suffered must be made through the Irish court system. Another important act is the Freedom of Information Act, which took effect in April 1998 [98]. The Act creates an Information Commissioner to enforce it. Misuse of data is also criminalized by the Criminal Damage Act 1991.

Ireland is a member of the Council of Europe and has signed and ratified the Convention for the Protection of Individuals with Regard to Automatic Processing of Personal Data and has signed and ratified the European Convention for the Protection of Human Rights and Fundamental Freedoms. It is also a member of the Organization for Economic Cooperation and Development and has adopted the OECD Guidelines on the Protection of Privacy and Transborder Flows of Personal Data.

7.9.   Italy

The Constitution has several provisions relating to privacy [99]. Article 14 states: "(1) Personal domicile is inviolable. (2) Inspection and search may not be carried out save in cases and in the manner laid down by law in conformity with guarantees prescribed for safeguarding personal freedom. (3) Special laws regulate verifications and inspections for reasons of public health and safety, or for economic and fiscal purposes." Article 15 states: "(1) The liberty and secrecy of correspondence and of every form of communication are inviolable. (2) Limitations upon them may only be enforced by decision, for which motives must be given, of the judicial authorities with the guarantees laid down by law."

The Italian Data Protection Act was enacted in 1996 [100, 101]. The Act is intended to fully implement the EU Data Protection Directive. It covers both electronic and manual files for both government agencies and the private sector. The Act is enforced by the Supervisory Authority ["Garante"] for Personal Data Protection. The Garante maintains a register, conducts audits, and enforces the laws and can also audit databanks not under its jurisdiction such as those relating to intelligence activities.

Italy is a member of the Council of Europe and has signed and ratified the Convention for the Protection of Individuals with Regard to Automatic Processing of Personal Data and has signed and ratified the European Convention for the Protection of Human Rights and Fundamental Freedoms. It is a member of the Organization for Economic Cooperation and Development and has adopted the OECD Guidelines on the Protection of Privacy and Transborder Flows of Personal Data.

7.10. Luxembourg

Article 28 of the Constitution of the Grand Duchy of Luxembourg states: "(1) The secrecy of correspondence is inviolable. The law determines the agents responsible for the violation of the secrecy of correspondence entrusted to the postal services. (2) The law determines the guarantee to be afforded to the secrecy of telegrams." [102]. Luxembourg's Act Concerning the Use of Nominal Data in Computer Processing was adopted in 1979 [103]. The law pertains to individually identifiable data in both public and private computer files. It also requires licensing of systems used for the processing of personal data. The law considers all personal data to be sensitive, although special provisions may be applied to medical and criminal information.

There is no general freedom of information law in Luxembourg. Under the 1960 decree on state archives, the archives are to be open to the public but citizens must make a written request explaining why they want access and ministers have broad discretion to deny requests.

For personal data processing by the private sector, an application must first be made to the Minister of Justice, who thereafter issues an authorization for such processing to take place. The Commission à la Protection des Données Nominatives, under the Ministry of Justice, oversees the law. If an application for personal data processing is granted, and there is an objection raised or if the application is refused or the original authorization is withdrawn for some reason, an appeal can be made to the Disputes Committee of the Council of State. A national register of all systems containing personal information is maintained by the Minister of Justice. Public sector personal data systems can be established only upon the issuance of a special law or regulation. In 1992, the law was amended to include special protection requirements for police and medical data. A bill that would make the law consistent with the EU Directive was introduced in the Parliament in 1997 but withdrawn in 1998. A project on electronic commerce that will implement the EU Telecommunications Privacy Directive was approved in 2000 [104, 105].

Luxembourg is a member of the Council of Europe and has signed and ratified the Convention for the Protection of Individuals with Regard to Automatic Processing of Personal Data and has signed and ratified the European Convention for the Protection of Human Rights and Fundamental Freedoms. It is a member of the Organization for Economic Cooperation and Development and has adopted the OECD Guidelines on the Protection of Privacy and Transborder Flows of Personal Data.

7.11. The Netherlands

The Constitution grants citizens an explicit right to privacy [106]. Article 10 states: "(1) Everyone shall have the right to respect for his privacy, without prejudice to restrictions laid down by or pursuant to Act of Parliament. (2) Rules to protect privacy shall be laid down by Act of Parliament in connection with the recording and dissemination of personal data. (3) Rules concerning the rights of persons to be informed of data recorded concerning them and of the use that is made thereof, and to have such data corrected shall be laid down by Act of Parliament." Article 13 states: "(1) The privacy of correspondence shall not be violated except, in the cases laid down by Act of Parliament, by order of the courts. (2) The privacy of the telephone and telegraph shall not be violated except, in the cases laid down by Act of Parliament, by or with the authorization of those designated for the purpose by Act of Parliament."

In May 2000, the government-appointed commission for "Constitutional rights in the digital age" presented proposals for changes to the Dutch constitution [107]. The commission was set up after confusion about the legal status of e-mail under the constitutionally protected privacy of letters. The commission's task was to investigate if existing constitutional rights should be made more technology-independent and if new rights should be introduced. As a result, the Personal Data Protection Act [108] of 2000 (Wet bescherming persoonsgegevens) was approved by the Parliament. This bill is a revised and expanded version of the 1988 Data Registration Act that will bring Dutch law in line with the European Data Protection Directive and will regulate the disclosure of personal data to countries outside of the European Union. The Act replaces the Data Registration Act of 1988 and went into effect in January 2001.

The Registration Chamber (Registratiekamer) serves as the Data Protection Authority and exercises supervision of the operation of personal data files in accordance with the Data Registration Act [109]. The Chamber advises the government, deals with complaints submitted by data subjects, institutes investigations, and makes recommendations to controllers of personal data files. There are presently over 60,000 databases registered with the Chamber. It has also released several reports on privacy-enhancing technologies jointly produced with the Office of the Information and Privacy Commissioner of Ontario, Canada. In June 2000, the Registration Chamber published a report on the privacy policies of Dutch Internet Service Providers (ISPs).

Two decrees were issued under the Data Registration Act. The Decree on Sensitive Data [110] sets out the limited circumstances when personal data on an individual's religious beliefs, race, political persuasion, sexuality, medical, psychological and criminal history may be included in a personal data file. The Decree on Regulated Exemption [111] exempts certain organizations from the registration requirements of the Data Registration Act. Interception of communications is regulated by the criminal code and requires a court order. A Telecommunications Act was approved in December 1998, which requires that ISPs have the capability by August 2000 to intercept all traffic with a court order and maintain user's logs for three months [112]. The Telecommunications Act also implements the EU Telecommunications Privacy Directive. There are sectoral laws dealing with the police, medical examinations [113], medical treatment [114], and social security data [115].

The Government Information (Public Access) Act is based on the constitutional right of access to information [116]. It states that documents created by a public agency should be available to everyone. Information can be withheld if it relates to international relations of the Dutch State, the "economic or financial interest of the State," investigation of criminal offenses, inspections by public authorities or personal privacy. However, these exemptions must be balanced against the importance of the disclosure. Requestors can appeal denials to an administrative court, which renders the final decision.

The Netherlands is a member of the Council of Europe and has signed and ratified the Convention for the Protection of Individuals with Regard to Automatic Processing of Personal Data and has signed and ratified the European Convention for the Protection of Human Rights and Fundamental Freedoms. It is a member of the Organization for Economic Cooperation and Development and has adopted the OECD Guidelines on the Protection of Privacy and Transborder Flows of Personal Data

7.12. Portugal

The Portuguese Constitution recognizes the right of privacy and private communications [117]. Article 35 states: "(1) Without prejudice to the provisions of the law on State secrecy and justice secrecy, all citizens have the right of access to the data contained in automated data records and files concerning them as well as the right to be informed of the use for which they are intended; they are entitled to request that the contents thereof be corrected and brought up to date. (2) Access to personal data records or files is forbidden for purposes of getting information relating to third parties as well as for the interconnection of these files, save in exceptional cases as provided for in the law and in Article 18. (3) Data processing may not be used in regard to information concerning a person's philosophical or political convictions, party or trade union affiliations, religious beliefs, or private life, except in the case of non-identifiable data for statistical purposes. (4) The law defines the concept of personal data for the purposes of data storage as well as the conditions for establishing data banks and data basis by public or private entities and the conditions of utilization and access. (5) Citizens may not be issued all-purpose national identification numbers. (6) The law defines the provisions applicable to transborder data flows establishing adequate norms of protection of personal data and of any other data in which the national interest is justified" [118].

A Data Protection Act (Lei da Protecção de Dados Pessoais) enacted in 1998 applies to automatic processing of personal data [119]. It requires that government agencies and private entities register their databases. There are limits on use and disclosure and data subjects have the right to access and correct their data. The Act is consistent with the EU Directive 95/46/EC. In 1998 a law was enacted (Lei nº 69/98) which regulates the treatment of personal data and privacy protection by the telecommunications sector consistent with the EU Directive 97/66/EC [120].

An independent agency, the National Data Protection Commission (Comissão Nacional de Protecção de Dados), enforces the Act [121]. The agency supervises registries established by public authorities and private enterprises in the country. It ensures that the conditions for registration, disclosure, and storage of data on individuals and on private enterprises are complied with. It mainly deals with specific cases on the basis of inquiries from public authorities or private individuals, or cases taken up by the agency on its own initiative.

Portugal is a member of the Council of Europe and has signed the Convention for the Protection of Individuals with Regard to Automatic Processing of Personal Data and has signed and ratified the European Convention for the Protection of Human Rights and Fundamental Freedoms. Portugal is a member of the Organization for Economic Cooperation and Development and has adopted the OECD Guidelines on the Protection of Privacy and Transborder Flows of Personal Data.

7.13. Spain

The Constitution recognizes the right to privacy, secrecy of communications and data protection. Article 18 states: "(1) The right of honor, personal, and family privacy and identity is guaranteed. (2) The home is inviolable. No entry or search may be made without legal authority except with the express consent of the owners or in the case of a *flagrante delicto*. (3) Secrecy of communications, particularly regarding postal, telegraphic, and telephone communication, is guaranteed, except for infractions by judicial order. (4) The law shall limit the use of information, to guarantee personal and family honor, the privacy of citizens, and the full exercise of their rights"; and Article 24.2 regulates the issue of secrecy [122].

Since the 80's and as consequence of economic and social pressures, there was a growing need for the health sector and healthcare organizations in Spain to improve their information and communication policies, strategies, programs, infrastructure, products, and services to facilitate patient data flow through the healthcare system. In 1985, Spain ratified the Council of Europe 1981 Convention for the Protection of Individuals with Regard to the Automatic Processing of Personal Data [55, 123].

The Spanish Data Protection Act (LORTAD) was enacted in 1992 [124] and amended in December 1999 [125] to implement the recommendations of the EU Data Protection Directive 95/46/EC. It covers files held by the public and private sector. The law establishes the right of citizens to know what personal data are contained in computer files and the right to correct or delete incorrect or false data. Personal information may be used or disclosed to a third party only with the consent of the individual and only for the purpose for which it was collected. Questions still remain about citizens who do not wish to be included in the "promotional census." Consumer groups are also concerned about the law provisions allowing use of information without consent unless the consumer has opted out of the use.

The Agencia de Protección de Datos [126] is charged with enforcing personal protection laws. The Agency maintains the registry and can investigate violations of the law. The agency has issued a number of decrees setting out in more detail the legal requirements for different types of information. It can also impose penalties. Interception of communications requires a court order.

The 1997 Telecommunications Act amended the law and restricts the use of cryptography but that provision has not been enforced. The law of 30/1992 provides for access to government information [127]. The law was amended in 1998 to state that the right of access and correction can be denied if reasons of public interest prevail. A number of civil laws regulate the right of privacy in health practice, national statistics, and dissemination of personal data [128, 129, 130, 131,132, 133, 134].

Spain is a member of the Council of Europe and has signed and ratified the Convention for the Protection of Individuals with Regard to Automatic Processing of Personal Data. It has signed and ratified the European Convention for the Protection of Human Rights and Fundamental Freedoms. It is a member of the Organization for Economic Cooperation and Development and has adopted the OECD Guidelines on the Protection of Privacy and Transborder Flows of Personal Data.

7.14. Sweden

Sweden's first data protection act dates back to the Riksdag's (Swedish Parliament) "Access to Public Records Act" of 1776. This Act is a "freedom of information act" in that the public was allowed to scrutinize public records for accuracy. It also served the purpose of ensuring that all government-held information was, in fact, required for legitimate purposes [77].

The Constitution, which consists of several different legal documents, contains several provisions that are relevant to data protection. Section 2 of the Instrument of Government Act of 1974 [135] provides, *inter alia*, for the protection of individual privacy. Section 13 of Chapter 2 of the same instrument states also that freedom of expression and information – which are constitutionally protected pursuant to the Freedom of the Press Act of 1949 – can be limited with respect to the "sanctity of private life." Moreover, Section 3 of the same chapter provides for a right to protection of personal integrity in relation to automatic data processing. The same article also prohibits non-consensual registration of persons purely on the basis of their political opinion. It is also important to note that the European Convention on Human Rights (ECHR) has been incorporated into Swedish law as of 1994. The ECHR is not formally part of the Swedish Constitution but has, in effect, similar status.

Sweden enacted the Personal Data Act of 1998 to bring Swedish law into conformity with the requirements of the EC Directive on data protection [136]. The new Act essentially adopts the EU Data Protection Directive into Swedish law. It regulates the establishment and use, in both public and private sectors, of automated data files on physical/natural persons. The Act replaced the Data Act of 1973, which was the first comprehensive national act on privacy in the world [137]. In contrast with the Data Act, the new act does not only apply to automated processing of personal data but in certain cases also to manual registers. However, the 1973 Act continued to apply until 1 October 2001 with respect to processing of personal data which was initiated prior to 24 October 1998. Section 33 of the Act was amended in 1999 to adopt the EU Directive standards on the transfer of personal data to a third country. The amendment entered into force in January 2000.

The Data Inspection Board (Datainspektionen) is an independent board that oversees the enforcement of the Data Act [138]. Numerous other statutes also contain provisions relating to data protection. These include the Secrecy Act of 1980, Credit Information Act of 1973, Debt Recovery Act of 1974, and Administrative Procedure Act of 1986.

Sweden is a member of the Council of Europe and has signed and ratified the Convention for the Protection of Individuals with Regard to Automatic Processing of Personal Data and has signed and ratified the European Convention for the Protection of Human Rights and Fundamental Freedoms. It is a member of the Organization for Economic Cooperation and Development and has adopted the OECD Guidelines on the Protection of Privacy and Transborder Flows of Personal Data.

7.15. United Kingdom

The privacy picture in the United Kingdom is mixed. There is, at some levels, a strong public recognition and defense of privacy. Proposals to establish a national identity card, for example, have routinely failed. On the other hand, crime and public order laws passed in recent years have placed substantial limitations on numerous rights, including freedom of assembly, privacy, freedom of movement, right of silence, and freedom of speech. There have been efforts for over twenty years to enact a Freedom of Information Act in the United Kingdom. A 1994 Code of Practice on Access to Government Information [139] provides some access to government records but has broad exemptions. Dissatisfied applicants can complain, via a Member of Parliament, to the Parliamentary Ombudsman if their request is denied.

In 1998, the Parliament approved the Human Rights Act that will incorporate the European Convention on Human Rights into domestic law, a process that will establish an enforceable right of privacy [140] The Act came into force on 2 October 2000. The Parliament approved and Royal Assent was given to the Data Protection Act (1998) in July 1998 [141]. The legislation, which came into force on March 1, 2000, updates the 1984 Data Protection Act [142] in accordance with the requirements of the European Union's Data Protection Directive 95/46/EC. The Act covers records held by government agencies and private entities. It provides for limitations on the use of personal information and access to records and requires that entities that maintain records register with the Data Protection Commissioner.

The Office of the Data Protection Commissioner is an independent agency that maintains the register and enforces the Act [143]. The Commissioner is also responsible for enforcing the Telecommunications (Data Protection and Privacy) Regulations. These regulations came into force on 1 March 2000, and fully implement the EU Telecommunications Directive. They repeal and replace the Telecommunications (Data Protection and Privacy) (Direct Marketing) Regulations 1998, which came into effect on 1 May 1999. The Commissioner issues a number of comprehensive reports for the public and has published a study of the availability and use of personal information in public registers [144]. There are also a number of other laws containing privacy components, most notably those governing medical records [145] and consumer credit information.

The Regulation of Investigatory Powers Act 2000 became law in July 2000 [146]. It provides powers for the Home Secretary to warrant interception of communications and to require Communications Service Providers to provide a "reasonable interception capability" in their networks. It further allows any public authority designated by the Home Secretary to access "communications data." These data include the source, destination and type of any communication, such as mobile phone location information. Finally, powers are provided for senior members of the civilian and military police, Customs, and members of the judiciary to require the plaintext of encrypted material, or in certain circumstances decryption keys themselves.

A Freedom of Information Bill was introduced into the House of Commons in November 1999. A draft of the legislation was released for public consultation in May 1999. The Act was amended and approved by the House of Commons in April 2000. The Bill is currently pending before the House of Lords. It has received considerable criticism from many politicians across the political spectrum and from non-governmental organizations as being insufficient and weaker than the existing code of practice. The law will create a new officer, the

Information Commissioner, to oversee both the Freedom of Information regime and the Data Protection Act 1998.

A document entitled "Good Practice Guidelines for General Practice Electronic Patient Records" [147], prepared by The Joint Computing Group of the General Practitioners and sponsored by the National Health Service Executive General and Personal Medical Services Branch, does an excellent job of outlining key attributes of electronic medical records. The guidelines are careful to note that many considerations applicable to paper records also are applicable to records in electronic form, and vice versa. A few, however, are only possible in electronic form. The guidelines list five differentiating characteristics for electronic health records (EHRs):

> **Physical** – While paper records exist independent of hardware and software, EHRs do not. Their physical presence is dependent upon the point at which the data are stored on a machine.

> **Accessibility** – While paper records must be physically delivered to the point of use, EHRs can be made available at any point where there is access to the electronic network and multiple users may have simultaneous access to a single electronic record stored elsewhere.

> **Resource** – In general, paper records are inexpensive when compared to EHRs, due in part to costs associated with hardware, software, communication tariffs, maintenance, upgrades, and training. File creation, storage, data security implementation, access control, and retrieval costs, however, may be lower and offset the higher costs of electronic records.

> **Predictability** – The use of paper records usually is predictable in that a health professional can move from one location to another without difficulty in reading from, or writing on, the paper document. EHRs may, in some cases, present problems when different locations employ differing technological platforms and interfaces or where certain added functions such as audits and decision support options, are not available at all locations.

Maintenance – Once they are filed, traditional paper records require little maintenance. EHRs require technical maintenance, upgrades, etc.

Training – Paper records typically are intuitive in their use. While a practitioner may receive training in the proper way to construct a paper medical record, there is normally little knowledge regarding the role and use of medical data processing. With EHRs, however, some degree of technical training in information science is often necessary. This may be especially true in situations where individual systems, as contrasted with compatible integrated systems, are maintained.

Too lengthy to reproduce herein, the guidelines also set forth a thorough analysis of elements critical to the operation of EHRs, including sections pertaining to: accessibility; storage; the use of coding schemes as a method of expressing clinical information; entry of data from remote sources; security policies; data integrity; record retention; medical confidentiality, and training. Although some of the recommendations are based upon the organizational and technical aspects employed by the United Kingdom National Health Service (NHS), their underlying rationales are probably applicable to a number of different systems. For instance, the concept of security incorporates at least four generic standards:

- **Availability** – is the EHR available upon demand and usable by those authorized?

- **Integrity** – is the EHR data accurate, without improper alteration or destruction? Is there an audit trail to document points of entry and modification?

- **Accountability** – can the actions relating to EHRs be sufficiently traced to ensure the authenticity of information and data entered?

- **Confidentiality** – is the information in the EHR maintained in such as way so as to prevent unauthorized disclosure to individuals, entities or technical processes?

It is important to note that no single law or regulation appears to protect every facet of electronic medical information. Rather, comprehensive protections are generated from numerable sources. For instance, the Guidelines observe that the majority of health information is held in confidence by the terms of the data protection Act of 1998 and the country's Common Law Duty of Confidence. This approach is similar to the actions taken by many countries seeking to generate the varied, yet necessary, protections for electronic health information.

In the light of the requirements in The Protection and Use of Patient Information and taking into account work undertaken by a joint Department of Health (DH) and British Medical Association (BMA) Working Group which considered the positions of the National Health Service Information Management and Technology (IM&T) in the areas of security and confidentiality, the Chief Medical Officer established the Caldicott Committee to review all patient-identifiable information that passes from National Health Service organizations to other NHS or non-NHS bodies for purposes other than direct care or medical research, or where there is a statutory requirement for information. The purpose was to ensure that patient identifiable information is transferred only for justified purposes and that only the minimum necessary information is transferred in each case. Where appropriate, the Committee was asked to advise whether action to minimize risks of breach of confidentiality would be desirable.

The work of the Committee was carried out in a consultative manner. Written submissions were sought from many organizations to identify existing concerns, and members of the Committee met with representatives of a number of key bodies. Working groups containing a wide range of health professionals and managers were established to consider related groups of information flows and to take soundings on emerging findings. About eighty-six flows of patient-identifiable information were mapped relating to a wide range of planning, operational, or monitoring purposes. Some of these flows were exemplars, representing locally diverse information flows with broadly similar characteristics and purposes. In 2001, the Caldicott Committee issued the following recommendations [28]:

- **Recommendation 1** - Every dataflow, current or proposed, should be tested against basic principles of good practice. Continuing flows should be re-tested regularly.

- **Recommendation 2** - A program of work should be established to reinforce awareness of confidentiality and information security requirements amongst all staff within the NHS.

- **Recommendation 3** - A senior person, preferably a health professional, should be nominated in each health organization to act as a guardian, responsible for safeguarding the confidentiality of patient information.

- **Recommendation 4** - Clear guidance should be provided for those individuals/bodies responsible for the approval of different uses of patient-identifiable information.

- **Recommendation 5** - Protocols should be developed to protect the exchange of patient-identifiable information between NHS and non-NHS bodies.

- **Recommendation 6** - The identity of those responsible for monitoring the sharing and transfer of information within agreed local protocols should be clearly communicated.

- **Recommendation 7** - An accreditation system which recognizes those organizations following good practice with respect to confidentiality should be considered.

- **Recommendation 8** - The NHS number should replace other identifiers wherever practicable, taking account of the consequences of errors and particular requirements for other specific identifiers.

- **Recommendation 9** - Strict protocols should define who is authorized to gain access to patient identity where the NHS number or other coded identifier is used.

- **Recommendation 10** - Where particularly sensitive information is transferred, privacy enhancing technologies (e.g., encrypting identifiers or "patient identifying information") must be explored.

- **Recommendation 11** - Those involved in developing health information systems should ensure that best practice principles are incorporated during the design stage.

- **Recommendation 12** - Where practicable, the internal structure and administration of databases holding patient-identifiable information should reflect the principles developed in this report.

- **Recommendation 13** - The NHS number should replace the patient's name on Items of Service Claims made by General Practitioners as soon as practically possible.

- **Recommendation 14** - The design of new systems for the transfer of prescription data should incorporate the principles developed in this report.

- **Recommendation 15** - Future negotiations on pay and conditions for General Practitioners should, where possible, avoid systems of payment that require patient identifying details to be transmitted.

- **Recommendation 16** - Consideration should be given to procedures for General Practice claims and payments which do not require patient-identifying information to be transferred, which can then be piloted.

The U.K. is a member of the Council of Europe and has signed and ratified the Convention for the Protection of Individuals with Regard to Automatic Processing of Personal Data along with the European

Convention for the Protection of Human Rights and Fundamental Freedoms. In addition to these commitments, the U.K. is a member of the Organization for Economic Cooperation and Development and has adopted the OECD Guidelines on the Protection of Privacy and Transborder Flows of Personal Data.

8. Review of Regulatory Responses: National Initiatives in European Countries Not Members of the European Union

8.1. Bulgaria

The Bulgarian Constitution of 1991 recognizes rights of privacy, secrecy of communications, and access to information. Article 32 states: "(1) The privacy of citizens shall be inviolable. Everyone shall be entitled to protection against any illegal interference in his private or family affairs and against encroachments on his honor, dignity and reputation. (2) No one shall be followed, photographed, filmed, recorded or subjected to any other similar activity without his knowledge or despite his express disapproval, except when such actions are permitted by law." Article 33 states: "(1) The home shall be inviolable. No one shall enter or stay inside a home without its occupant's consent, except in the cases expressly stipulated by law. (2) Entry into, or staying inside, a home without the consent of its occupant or without the judicial authorities' permission shall be allowed only for the purposes of preventing an immediately impending crime or a crime in progress, for the capture of a criminal, or in extreme necessity." Article 34 states: "(1) The freedom and confidentiality of correspondence and all other communications shall be inviolable. (2) Exceptions to this provision shall be allowed only with the permission of the judicial authorities for the purpose of discovering or preventing a grave crime." Article 41 states: "(1) Everyone shall be entitled to seek, obtain and disseminate information. This right shall not be exercised to the detriment of the rights and reputation of others, or to the detriment of national security, public order, public health and morality. (2) Citizens shall be entitled to obtain information from state bodies and agencies on any matter of legitimate interest to them which is not a state or other secret prescribed by law and does not affect the rights of others" [148].

There are currently efforts to enact comprehensive data protection legislation in Bulgaria. In 1996, the government began developing data protection legislation in preparation for integration into the EU Internal Market under the Treaty for Association of Bulgaria to the EU. Data protection is also a key element of the information legislation, which is a priority in the National Assembly's legislative activities. The draft Personal Data Protection Act closely follows the EU Data Protection Directive. It sets rules on the fair and responsible handling of personal information by the public and private sector.

Entities collecting personal information must inform people why their personal information is being collected and what it is to be used for; allow people reasonable access to information about themselves and the right to correct it if it is wrong; ensure that the information is securely held and cannot be tampered with, stolen, or improperly used; and limit the use of personal information, for purposes other than the original purpose, without the consent of the person affected, or in certain other circumstances. The draft law creates a State Commission for the Protection of Personal Data to oversee the act. The Law for Access to Information to provide access to government records was enacted in June 2000 [149]. The law allows for access to records except in cases of state security or personal privacy.

Bulgaria is a member of the Council of Europe and has signed but not ratified the Convention for the Protection of Individuals with Regard to Automatic Processing of Personal Data. It has signed and ratified the European Convention for the Protection of Human Rights and Fundamental Freedoms.

8.2. Estonia

The Constitution of the Republic of Estonia recognizes the right of privacy, secrecy of communications, and data protection. Article 42 states: "No state or local government authority or their officials may collect or store information on the persuasions of any Estonian citizen against his or her free will." Article 43 states: "Everyone shall be entitled to secrecy of messages transmitted by him or to him by post, telegram, telephone or other generally used means. Exceptions may be made on authorization by a court, in cases and in accordance with procedures determined by law in order to prevent a criminal act or for the purpose of establishing facts in a criminal investigation." Article 44 (3): states, "Estonian citizens shall have the right to become acquainted with information about themselves held by state and local government authorities and in state and local government archives, in accordance with procedures determined by law. This right may be restricted by law in order to protect the rights and liberties of other persons, and the secrecy of children's ancestry, as well as to prevent a crime, or in the interests of apprehending a criminal or to clarify the truth for a court case" [150].

The Riigikogu – Estonia's Parliament – enacted the Personal Data Protection Act in June 1996 [151]. The Act protects the fundamental rights and freedoms of persons with respect to the processing of personal data and in accordance with the right of individuals to obtain freely any information that is disseminated for public use. The Personal Data Protection Act divides personal data into two groups – non-sensitive and sensitive personal data. Sensitive personal data are data that reveal political opinions, religious or philosophical beliefs, ethnic or racial origin, health, sexual life, criminal convictions, legal punishments, and involvement in criminal proceedings. Processing of non-sensitive personal data is permitted without the consent of the respective individual if it occurs under the terms that are set out in the Personal Data Protection Act. Processed personal data are protected by organizational and technical measures that must be documented.

In April 1997, the Riigikogu passed the Databases Act [152]. The Databases Act is a procedural law for the establishment of national databases. The law sets out the general principles for the maintenance of databases, prescribes requirements and protection measures for data processing, and unifies the terminology to be used in the maintenance of databases.

Pursuant to the Databases Act, the statutes of state registers or databases that were created before the law took effect must be brought into line with the Act within two years. The Databases Act also mandates the establishment of a state register of databases for state and local government databases, as well as databases containing sensitive personal data that are maintained by private persons or organizations. The Data Protection Inspectorate is the supervisory authority for the Personal Data Protection Act and the Databases Act. The Inspectorate, a division of the Ministry of Internal Affairs, monitors compliance, issues licenses, takes complaints, and settles disputes. The agency can conduct investigations and demand documents, impose fines, and impose administrative sanctions [153]. Data processing organizations must register the processing of sensitive personal data with the data protection supervision authority. The Digital Signatures Act was approved in March 2000 [154].

Estonia is a member of the Council of Europe and signed the Convention for the Protection of Individuals with Regard to Automatic Processing of Personal Data. Estonia has signed and ratified the European Convention for the Protection of Human Rights and Fundamental Freedoms.

8.3.   Greenland

The original unamended Danish Public and Private Registers Acts [73, 74] continue to apply within Greenland, a self-governing territory. The amendments that brought Denmark into compliance with the Council of Europe's Convention do not apply to Greenland. Greenland is not part of the European Union and therefore has not adopted the EU Privacy Directive. Greenland's data protection requirements are much less stringent than those of Denmark and the other nations of the EU.

8.4.   Hungary

Article 59 of the Constitution of the Republic of Hungary reads, "Everyone in the Republic of Hungary shall have the right to good reputation, the inviolability of the privacy of his home and correspondence, and the protection of his personal data" [155]. In 1991, the Supreme Court ruled that a law creating a multi-use personal identification number violated the constitutional right of privacy [156].

In 1992 an act was enacted on the Protection of Personal Data and Disclosure of Data of Public Interest. This Act covers the collection and use of personal information in both the public sector and private sector [157]. It is a combined Data Protection and Freedom of Information Act. Its basic principle is informational self-determination. As Hungary is an applicant for EU membership only minor changes are required to make the Act compliant with the EU Directive. In June 1999, the Parliament amended the Act to treat data controllers and data processors differently to make it more consistent with the EU Directive [158].

The Parliamentary Commissioner for Data Protection and Freedom of Information oversees the 1992 Act [159]. Besides acting as an ombudsman for both data protection and freedom of information, the Commissioner's tasks include maintaining the Data Protection Register and providing opinions on related draft legislation, as well as each category of official secrets. Under the Secrecy Act of 1995, the Commissioner is entitled to change the classification of state and official secrets as well. The Commission has been very active reviewing cases involving personal information.

Many laws contain rules for handling personal data, including addresses [160], universal identifiers [161], medical information [162], public records [163], and telecommunications [164]. The Direct Marketing Act provides for opt-out, but only for name and address information [165]. There is no sectoral legislation covering the Internet.

Hungary is a member of the Council of Europe and has signed and ratified the Convention for the Protection of Individuals with Regard to Automatic Processing of Personal Data. It has signed and ratified the European Convention for the Protection of Human Rights and Fundamental Freedoms. It is a member of the Organization for Economic Cooperation and Development and has adopted the OECD Guidelines on the Protection of Privacy and Transborder Flows of Personal Data.

8.5.   Iceland

Section 72 of the Constitution of Iceland states: "The dwelling shall be inviolable. House searching, seizure, and examination of letters and other papers as well as any breach of the secrecy to be observed in postal, telegraph, and telephone matters shall take place only under a judicial order unless particular exception is warranted by Statute [166].

The Act on Protection of Individuals with regard to the Processing of Personal Data regulates the processing of personal information for government agencies and corporations enacted to ensure compliance with the EU Directive [167]. The Act covers both automated and manual processing of personal information. It also covers video surveillance and limits the use of National Identification Numbers. The Statistical Bureau of Iceland shall maintain a registry of individuals not willing to allow the use of their names in product marketing. It replaces the 1989 Act on the Registration and Handling on Personal Data [168]. The Act is enforced by the Icelandic Data Protection Commission (Datatilsynet). The Commission maintains the registry of activities and can investigate and issue rulings. It can also impose fines for non-compliance and can seek criminal sanctions. The Authority can also prohibit or mandate the use of the National Identification Numbers.

In December 1998, the Parliament approved a bill to create a nationwide centralized health database to be used for genetic research [169]. The Government gave an exclusive 12-year license for the database to the American biotechnology company deCODE Genetics, which will create a nationwide genetic database of the entire Icelandic population based on 30 years of patients' records. Patients were originally required to opt out of the database by June 1999. After that date, their information could not be removed. Pressed by criticism from the EU, the Government enacted the Act on Biobanks on 13 May 2000 [170]. The act sets rules for the "collection, keeping, handling and utilization of biological samples from human beings" to ensure confidentiality and prohibit discrimination. The Act requires informed consent from the person for the collection of samples. However, under the Act "if samples have been collected for the purpose of clinical tests or treatment, the consent of the patient may be assumed for the storage of the biological sample in a biobank," if the doctor gives general information to the patient.

The Freedom of Information Act of 1996 (Upplysingalög) governs the release of records [171]. Under the Act, individuals including non-residents and legal entities, have a legal right to documents without having to show a reason for the document. There are exceptions for national security, commercial, and personal information.

Iceland is a member of the Council of Europe and has signed
and ratified the Convention for the Protection of Individuals with Regard
to Automatic Processing of Personal Data and has signed and ratified
the European Convention for the Protection of Human Rights and
Fundamental Freedoms. It is a member of the Organization for
Economic Cooperation and Development and has adopted the OECD
Guidelines on the Protection of Privacy and Transborder Flows of
Personal Data. Iceland is not an EU member state but has been granted
associate status.

8.6.   Latvia

Freedom of expression is granted by the Satversme
(Constitution of Latvia). Article 17 of the Constitutional Law on Rights
and Obligations of a Citizen and a Person states: "(1) The State
guarantees the confidentiality of correspondence, telephone
conversations, telegraph and other communications. (2) These rights
may be restricted by a judge's order for the investigation of serious
crimes" [172].

Privacy, data protection, and consumer protection are covered
by a draft law on Personal Data Protection, which has passed the
second reading in the Saeima (Parliament), and the law on Consumer
Protection is in effect as of March 1999 [173]. Electronic protection,
legal protection and security (encryption, electronic commerce) have not
been thus far addressed by legislative acts. The Law on Freedom of
Information is in effect as of October 1998 [174]. The Law requires
information of Government bodies and local governments to be freely
accessible unless it is in conflict with other law.

The Law on Personal Data Protection was adopted by the
Parliament on 23 March 2000. The law is based on the EU Data
Directive and the Council of Europe Convention No. 108. The bill will
also create a Data Protection Inspectorate. The approval follows several
years of EU pressure to adopt the law.

Latvia is a member of the Council of Europe and signed the
Convention for the Protection of Individuals with Regard to Automatic
Processing of Personal Data and has signed and ratified the European

Convention for the Protection of Human Rights and Fundamental
Freedoms.

8.7.   Lithuania

Article 22 of the Constitution states: "The private life of an
individual shall be inviolable. Personal correspondence, telephone
conversations, telegraph messages, and other intercommunications
shall be inviolable. Information concerning the private life of an individual
may be collected only upon a justified court order and in accordance
with the law. The law and the court shall protect individuals from
arbitrary or unlawful interference in their private or family life, and from
encroachment upon their honor and dignity" [175].

Lithuania enacted its Law on Legal Protection of Personal Data
in 1996 [176] and amended it in March 1998 to extend it to
computerized information held by the private sector [177]. The Law
regulates the processing of all types of personal data, not just in state
information systems. It defines the time and the general means of
protecting personal data and sets rights of access and correction. It also
sets rules on the collecting, processing, transferring, and using of data.
The Administrative Code defines various monetary penalties in cases of
the infringement of the processing and use of data.

There is also a Law on Public Registers [178] that governs the
use and legitimacy of state data registers that contain person-identifiable
information. The law also mandates that data registers may only be
erased or destroyed in cooperation with the State Data Protection
Inspectorate. The Parliament is reviewing extensive amendments to the
law [179]. The amendments would ensure the law's compliance with the
EU Directives on Data Protection and Telecommunications. It will cover
not just the processing of personal information by computers, but also
by other means. It also adopts the Council of Europe recommendations
on direct marketing, healthcare, science research, telecommunications,
and statistics.

The State Data Protection Inspectorate was established in 1996
to enforce the provisions of the Law on Legal Protection of Personal
Data and the Law on State Registers [180, 181]. It registers data

controllers, supervises processing, handles appeals for denial of access to records, and approves transborder data flows. There are specific privacy protections in laws relating to telecommunications [182], statistics [183], the population register [184], and health information [185]. The 1996 Law on the Provision of Information to the Public provides for a limited right of access to official documents and to documents held by political parties, political and public organizations, trade unions and other entities [186]. A more comprehensive law on the Right to Receive Information from the State and Municipal Institutions drafted by the Lithuanian Center for Human Rights is currently being reviewed by the Parliament.

Lithuania is in the process of preparing for membership in the EU and has a National Program for the Adoption of EU Regulations. It is a member of the Council of Europe but has not yet signed and ratified the Convention for the Protection of Individuals with Regard to Automatic Processing of Personal Data. It has signed and ratified the European Convention for the Protection of Human Rights and Fundamental Freedoms.

8.8. Norway

There is no provision in the Norwegian Constitution of 1814 dealing specifically with the protection of privacy [187]. The closest provision is Section 102, which prohibits searches of private homes except in "criminal cases." More generally, Section 110c of the Constitution places state authorities under an express duty to "respect and secure human rights." The Norwegian Supreme Court has held that there exists in Norwegian law a general legal protection of "personality" which embraces a right to privacy. This protection of personality exists independently of statutory authority but helps form the basis of the latter, including data protection legislation, and can be applied by the courts on a case-by-case basis.

The Personal Data Registers Act of 2000 was approved on April 2000 [188]. It is designed to update Norwegian law and closely follows the EU Directive, even though Norway is not a member of the EU. The new law also sets specific rules on video surveillance and biometrics. It replaces the Personal Data Registers Act of 1978 [189].

The Data Inspectorate (Datatilsynet) is an independent administration body set up under the Ministry of Justice in 1980. The Inspectorate accepts applications for licenses for data registers and evaluates the licenses, enforces the privacy laws and regulations, and provides information. The Inspectorate can conduct inspections and impose sanctions [190].

The Telecommunications Act imposes a duty of confidentiality on telecommunications providers [191]. A large number of other pieces of legislation contain provisions relevant to privacy and data protection. These include the Administrative Procedures Act of 1967 and the Criminal Code of 1902. The Freedom of Information Act regulates public access to documents in the public administration and to government records [192]. Under the Act, there is a broad right of access to records.

Norway is a member of the Council of Europe and has signed and ratified the Convention for the Protection of Individuals with Regard to Automatic Processing of Personal Data and has signed and ratified the European Convention for the Protection of Human Rights and Fundamental Freedoms. It is a member of the Organization for Economic Cooperation and Development and has adopted the OECD Guidelines on the Protection of Privacy and Transborder Flows of Personal Data. Norway is a party to the 1992 Agreement on the European Economic Area (EEA). As such, it is required to comply with the EU Directive before it is formally incorporated into the EEA.

8.9. Poland

The Polish Constitution recognizes the rights of privacy and data protection. Article 47 states: "Everyone shall have the right to legal protection of his private and family life, of his honor and good reputation and to make decisions about his personal life." Article 51 states: "(1) No one may be obliged, except on the basis of statute, to disclose information concerning his person. (2) Public authorities shall not acquire, collect nor make accessible information on citizens other than that which is necessary in a democratic state ruled by law. (3) Everyone shall have a right of access to official documents and data collections concerning him/herself. Limitations upon such rights may be established by statute. (4) Everyone shall have the right to demand the correction or deletion of untrue or incomplete information, or information acquired by means contrary to statute. (5) Principles and procedures for collection of and access to information shall be specified by statute" [193].

The Law on the Protection of Personal Data Protection was approved in October 1997 and took effect in April 1998 [194]. The law is based on the European Union Data Protection Directive. Under the Law, personal information may be processed only with the consent of the individual. Everyone has the right to verify his or her personal records held by government agencies or private companies. Every citizen has the right to be informed whether such databases exist and who administers them; queries should be answered within thirty days. Upon finding out that data are incorrect, inaccurate, outdated or collected in a way that constitutes a violation of the Act, citizens have the right to request that the data be corrected, filled in or withheld from processing. Personal information cannot generally be transferred outside of Poland unless the country has "comparable" protections. A 1998 regulation from the Minister of Internal Affairs and Administration sets out standards for the security of information systems that contain personal information.

The Act is enforced by the Bureau of Inspector General for the Protection of Personal Data [195]. The Bureau maintains a register of data files and can make checks on the basis of a complaint or by random inspections. The Bureau is also responsible for registering databases. An inspector has the right to access data, check data transfer and security systems, and determine whether the information gathered is appropriate for the purpose that it is supposed to serve. The office monitors the activities of all central government, local government and private institutions, individuals, and corporations.

Poland enacted the Classified Information Protection Act in January 1999 as a condition to entering NATO [196]. The Act covers classified information or information collected by government agencies whose disclosure "might damage interests of the state, public interests, or lawfully protected interests of citizens or of an organization."

Poland is a member of the Council of Europe and signed the Convention for the Protection of Individuals with Regard to Automatic Processing of Personal Data but has not yet ratified it. Poland has signed and ratified the European Convention for the Protection of Human Rights and Fundamental Freedoms. Poland is a member of the Organization for Economic Cooperation and Development and has adopted the OECD Guidelines on the Protection of Privacy and Transborder Flows of Personal Data.

8.10. Russia

The Constitution of the Russian Federation recognizes rights of privacy, data protection and secrecy of communications. Article 23 states: "(1) Everyone shall have the right to privacy, to personal and family secrets, and to protection of one's honor and good name. (2) Everyone shall have the right to privacy of correspondence, telephone communications, mail, cables and other communications. Any restriction of this right shall be allowed only under an order of a court of law." Article 24 states: "(1) It shall be forbidden to gather, store, use and disseminate information on the private life of any person without his/her consent. (2) The bodies of state authority and the bodies of local self-government and the officials thereof shall provide to each citizen access to any documents and materials directly affecting his/her rights and liberties unless otherwise stipulated under the law." Article 25 states: "The home shall be inviolable. No one shall have the right to enter the home against the will of persons residing in it except in cases stipulated by the federal law or under an order of a court of law" [197].

In 1985, the Duma approved the Law of the Russian Federation on Information, Informatization, and Information Protection [198]. The law covers both the government and private sectors and licenses the processing of personal information by the private sector. It imposes a code of fair information practices on the processing of personal information. It prohibits the use of personal information to "inflict economic or moral damage on citizens." The use of sensitive information such as social origin, race, nationality, language, religion, or party membership is also prohibited. Citizens and organizations have the right of access to the documented information about them, to correct it and supplement it.

The Law of the Russian Federation on Information, Informatization, and Information Protection also serves as a Freedom of

Information law. The law specifies that responsibility for data protection rests with the data controllers. The law is overseen by the Committee of the State Duma on Information and Informatization and the State Committee on Information and Informatization under the Russian President Authority. The scope of the law is generally limited.

A more broad bill entitled "Federal Law on the Right to Access Information" is currently pending in the Duma. The Duma is reviewing the Law on Information of Personal Character bill to update the 1995 act to make it more compliant with the Council of Europe's Convention 108 and the EU Directive. The bill creates a presumption that information is "available and open," "reliable and complete," and "must be timely disclosed." Agencies must respond within thirty days. Information can be withheld if it is a "national, commercial, official, professional or banking secret" or related to a "valid investigation and fact-finding proceedings." If information is withheld, the person can appeal to the agency, then to a court and the Human Rights Ombudsman.

Secrecy of communications is protected by the 1995 Communications Act. The tapping of telephone conversations, scrutiny of electronic-communications messages, delay, inspection and seizure of postal mailings and documentary correspondence, receipt of information therein, and other restriction of communications secrets are allowed only on the basis of a court order [199]. There are also privacy protections in the Civil Code [200] and the Criminal Code [201].

Russia is a member of the Council of Europe but has not signed and ratified the Convention for the Protection of Individuals with Regard to Automatic Processing of Personal Data. Russia signed and ratified the European Convention for the Protection of Human Rights and Fundamental Freedoms.

8.11. Slovakia

The 1992 Constitution of the Slovak Republic provides for protections for privacy, data protection, and secrecy of communications. Article 16 states: "(1) The inviolability of the person and its privacy is guaranteed. It can be limited only in cases defined by law." Article 19 states: "(1) Everyone has the right to the preservation of his human dignity and personal honor, and the protection of his good name. (2) Everyone has the right to protection against unwarranted interference in his private and family life. (3) Everyone has the right to protection against the unwarranted collection, publication, or other illicit use of his personal data." Article 22 states: "(1) The privacy of correspondence and secrecy of mailed messages and other written documents and the protection of personal data are guaranteed. (2) No one must violate the privacy of correspondence and the secrecy of other written documents and records, whether they are kept in private or sent by mail or in another way, with the exception of cases to be set out in a law. Equally guaranteed is the secrecy of messages conveyed by telephone, telegraph, or other similar means" [202].

The Act on Protection of Personal Data in Information Systems was approved in February 1998 and went into effect in March 1998 [203, 204]. The Act replaces the previous 1992 Czechoslovakian legislation on the protection of personal data [205]. The new act closely follows the EU Data Protection Directive and limits the collection, disclosure, and use of personal information by government agencies and private enterprises in either electronic or manual form. It creates duties of access, accuracy, and correction, security, and confidentiality on the data processor. Processing of information on racial, ethnic, political opinions, religion, philosophical beliefs, trade union membership, health, and sexuality is forbidden. Transfers to other countries are limited unless the country has "adequate" protection. All systems are required to be registered with the Statistical Office of the Slovak Republic [206]. The Act creates a new office for a Commissioner for the Protection of Personal Data in Information Systems who will supervise and enforce the Act. The Commission monitors the protection of personal data in information systems and their registration, inspects the processing of personal data in information systems, receives and handles complaints concerning the violation of personal data protection in information systems, and initiates corrective actions whenever a breach of legal obligations is ascertained. The Commission has an Inspection Unit for Personal Data Protection, which carries out supervision of tasks. There are also other legal protections. Article 11 of the Civil Code states: "Everyone shall have the right to be free from unjustified interference in his or her privacy and family life." There are also computer-related offenses linked with the protection of a person, like the unjustified treatment of a personal data.

The Act on Free Access to Information was approved by the Parliament in May 2000 [207]. It sets broad rules on disclosure of information held by the government. There are limitations on information that is classified, a trade secret, would violate privacy, was obtained "from a person not required by law to provide information, who upon notification of the Obligee instructed the Obligee in writing not to disclose information," or "concerns the decision-making power of the courts and law enforcement bodies." Appeals are made to higher agencies and can be reviewed by a court. There are separate requirements for disclosure of environmental information that covers private organizations. It became effective 1 January 2001.

Slovakia is a member of the Council of Europe and signed the Convention for the Protection of Individuals with Regard to Automatic Processing of Personal Data in April 2000. It has signed and ratified the European Convention for the Protection of Human Rights and Fundamental Freedoms.

8.12. Slovenia

The 1991 Constitution of the Republic of Slovenia recognizes many privacy rights. Article 35 on the Protection of the Right to Privacy and of Personal Rights states: "The physical and mental integrity of each person shall be guaranteed, as shall be his right to privacy and his other personal rights." Article 37 on the Protection of Privacy of Post and Other Means of Communication states: "The privacy of the post and of other means of communication shall be guaranteed. In accordance with statute, a court may authorize action infringing on the privacy of the post or of other means of communication, or on the inviolability of individual privacy, where such actions are deemed necessary for the institution or continuance of criminal proceedings or for reasons of national security." Article 38 on the Protection of Personal Data states: "The protection of personal data relating to an individual shall be guaranteed. Any use of personal data shall be forbidden where that use conflicts with the original purpose for which it was collected. The collection, processing and the end-use of such data, as well as the supervision and protection of the confidentiality of such data, shall be regulated by statute. Each person has the right to be informed of the personal data relating to him which has been collected and has the right to legal remedy in the event of any misuse of same" [208].

A new Law on Personal Data Protection [209] went into effect in August 1999 and is based on the EU Data Protection Directive and the Community of Europe Convention ETS No. 108 [55]. The implementation of the law will create an "Inspectorate" to supervise and enforce dispositions. The previous law [210] had limited oversight of personal data protection practices. The Law on National Statistics regulates the privacy of information collected for statistical purposes [211]. The Law on Telecommunications [212] requires telecommunications service providers to "guarantee the confidentiality of transmitted messages and of personal and non-personal data known only to them", however, privacy and data protection in telecommunications and Internet are treated rather inconsistently. The Electronic Commerce and Electronic Signature Act was approved in June 2000 [213]. A Law on Databases in the Healthcare Sector is being discussed at the National Assembly.

Slovenia is a member of the Council of Europe and has signed and ratified the Convention for the Protection of Individuals with Regard to Automatic Processing of Personal Data and has also signed and ratified the European Convention for the Protection of Human Rights and Fundamental Freedoms.

8.13. Switzerland

Article 36(4) of the 1874 Swiss Confederation Constitution already guaranteed "the inviolability of the secrecy of letters and telegrams" [214]. This Constitution was replaced by public referendum in April 1999 and the new constitution, which entered into force on 1 January 2000, greatly expanded the older privacy protection provision. Article 13 of the Constitution now states: "All persons have the right to receive respect for their private and family life, home, mail and telecommunications. All persons have the right to be protected against abuse of their personal data" [215].

The Federal Act of Data Protection of 1992 regulates personal information held by government and private bodies [216]. The Act requires that information must be legally and fairly collected and places limits on its use and disclosure to third parties. Private companies must register if they regularly process sensitive data or transfer the data to third parties. Transfers to other nations must be registered and the recipient nation must have equivalent laws. Individuals have a right of access to correct inaccurate information. Federal agencies must register their databases. There are criminal penalties for violations. There are also separate data protection acts for the Cantons (states). In June 1999, the European Union Data Protection Working Party determined that Swiss law was adequate under the EU Directive [217]. In July 2000, the European Commission formally adopted this position, thereby approving all future transfers of all personal data transfers to Switzerland.

The 1992 Act created a Federal Data Protection Commission [218]. The Commission maintains and publishes the Register for Data Files, supervises federal government and private bodies, provides advice, issues recommendations and reports, and conducts investigations. The Commissioner also consults with the private sector. Its most recent report recommended improvements in telecommunications privacy, controls on workplace monitoring, legal limitations on DNA databases, the development of strong privacy-enhancing technologies, and greater consumer protections in the areas of unwanted telemarketing, Caller-ID, spamming, online profiling, and data mining. It also recommended increased cooperation at the international level to protect privacy and the introduction of legislation, similar to that in Germany, providing an explicit right to anonymity. Telecommunications are governed by the Penal Code and Penal Procedure Code amended by the 1997 Telecommunication Act that came into effect on 1 January 1998 [219].

Besides the Data Protection Act, there are also legal protections for privacy in the Civil Code [220] and Penal Code [221], and special rules relating to the protection of workers' privacy from surveillance, telecommunications information [222], healthcare statistics [223], professional confidentiality including medical and legal information, medical research [224], police files [225, 226, 227], and identity cards [228].

Switzerland is a member of the Council of Europe and signed and ratified the Convention for the Protection of Individuals with Regard to Automatic Processing of Personal Data and the European Convention for the Protection of Human Rights and Fundamental Freedoms. Switzerland is a member of the Organization for Economic Cooperation and Development and has adopted the OECD Guidelines on the Protection of Privacy and Transborder Flows of Personal Data. Switzerland is not an EU member state but has been granted associate status.

8.14. Turkey

Section Five of the 1982 Turkish Constitution is entitled "Privacy and Protection of Private Life" [291]. Article 20 of the Turkish Constitution deals with "Privacy of the Individual's Life," and it states: "Everyone has the right to demand respect for his private and family life. Privacy of individual and family life cannot be violated. Exceptions necessitated by judiciary investigation and prosecution are reserved. Unless there exists a decision duly passed by a judge in cases explicitly defined by law, and unless there exists an order of an agency authorized by law in cases where delay is deemed prejudicial, neither the person nor the private papers, nor belongings of an individual shall be searched nor shall they be seized." Article 22 states: "Secrecy of communication is fundamental. Communication shall not be impeded nor its secrecy be violated, unless there exists a decision duly passed by a judge in cases explicitly defined by law, and unless there exists an order of an agency authorized by law in cases where delay is deemed prejudicial. Public establishments or institutions where exceptions to the above may be applied will be defined by law."

The Turkish Ministry of Justice as of the summer of 2000 has been working on the draft of legislation addressing the protection of personal data. A working group was established to draft a Turkish Data Protection law based on proposals discussed within the May 1998 E-Commerce Laws Working Party Report [292]. The proposed law emphasizes both the importance of facilitating the collection and processing of personal data and the protection of personal data of individuals in the information age. There is no criminal liability for such violations of personal rights and currently there is no protection for personal data under the Turkish Criminal Code.

Turkey is a member of the Council of Europe and has accepted the Council's monitoring mechanism. It signed the Convention for the Protection of Individuals with Regard to Automatic Processing of Personal Data in 1981 but has not ratified the act. It has signed and ratified the European Convention for the Protection of Human Rights and Fundamental Freedoms. Turkey has also been a member of the Organization for Economic Cooperation and Development since 1961.

8.15. Ukraine

The Constitution of the Republic of Ukraine guarantees the right of privacy and data protection [229]. Article 31 states: "Everyone is guaranteed privacy of mail, telephone conversations, telegraph and other correspondence. Exceptions shall be established only by a court in cases envisaged by law, with the purpose of preventing crime or ascertaining the truth in the course of the investigation of a criminal case, if it is not possible to obtain information by other means." Article 32 states: "No one shall be subject to interference in his or her personal and family life, except in cases envisaged by the Constitution of Ukraine. The collection, storage, use and dissemination of confidential information about a person without his or her consent shall not be permitted, except in cases determined by law, and only in the interests of national security, economic welfare and human rights. Every citizen has the right to examine information about himself or herself, that is not a state secret or other secret protected by law, at the bodies of state power, bodies of local self-government, institutions and organizations. Everyone is guaranteed judicial protection of the right to rectify incorrect information about himself or herself and members of his or her family, and of the right to demand that any type of information be expunged, and also the right to compensation for material and moral damages inflicted by the collection, storage, use and dissemination of such incorrect information." There is also a limited right of freedom of information. Article 50 states: "Everyone is guaranteed the right of free access to information about the environmental situation, the quality of food and consumer goods, and also the right to disseminate such information. No one shall make such information secret."

The Act "On Information" defines only general principles of citizens' access to information personally related to them. Article 9 provides individuals with access to information concerning them. Exceptions are to be defined by Law. Article 23 of the Statute prohibits collection of personal data without consent of the data subject, and provides the right to know about data collection [230]. The Constitutional Court of Ukraine ruled in October 1997 that Article 23 prohibited not only the collection of information, but also the storage, use and dissemination of confidential personal information without the consent of the individual [231]. There are exceptions for national security, economic wellbeing, and information that would affect another's rights and freedoms. Confidential information includes, in particular, information about a person such as education, marital status, state of health, date and place of birth, property status, and other personal details.

The 1992 Act on Information provides a right of access to government records. Article 21 sets out methods for making official information public, including disclosing it to interested persons orally, in writing, or in other ways. Article 29 of the Statute prohibits the limitation of the right to obtain non-covert information. Article 37 sets out a long list of exceptions. The author of a rejected or postponed request has a right to appeal against the decision to a higher echelon or court (Article 34).

Currently there is an effort to enact a broader data protection act. The draft bill on Data Protection prepared by State Committee of Communications and Computerization was introduced to the Cabinet of Ministers and is loosely based on the Council of Europe Convention No. 108 and the State of Hesse's (Germany) 1970 data protection act and focuses on property rights for privacy control. The original drafts proposed the establishment of a Data Protection Ombudsman but the most recent draft leaves out the office because of opposition by the State Security Service and Ministry of Justice. There are a number of other laws that control personal information [232]. There are laws relating to tax information, social insurance, domicile registration, retirement insurance, unemployment insurance, criminal investigations, juvenile records, former prisoners, military service records, medical records [233], and HIV records [234].

Ukraine is a member of the Council of Europe but has not signed or ratified the Convention for the Protection of Individuals with Regard to Automatic Processing of Personal Data. It has signed and ratified the European Convention for the Protection of Human Rights and Fundamental Freedoms.

9. Review of Regulatory Responses: National Initiatives in the Americas

9.1. Argentina

Articles 18 and 19 of the Argentine Constitution provide: "The home is inviolable as is personal correspondence and private papers; the law will determine what cases and what justifications may be relevant to their search or confiscation. The private actions of men that in no way offend order nor public morals, nor prejudice a third party, are reserved only to God's judgment, and are free from judicial authority. No inhabitant of the Nation will be obligated to do that which is not required by law, nor be deprived of what is not prohibited." Article 43, enacted in 1994, provides a right of *habeas data*: "Every person may file an action to obtain knowledge of the data about them and its purpose, whether contained in public or private registries or databases intended to provide information; and in the case of false data or discrimination, to suppress, rectify, make confidential, or update the data. The privacy of news information sources may not be affected" [235].

In 1994, Argentina adopted the American Convention on Human Rights into domestic law. The Argentine Supreme Court has used international human law to determine domestic cases. In November 1998 the Senate approved a Law for the Protection of Personal Data [236]. It is in conformance with Article 43 of the Constitution and based on the European Union Data Protection Directive. The bill covers electronic and manual records. It requires express consent before information can be collected, stored, processed, or transferred. Collection of sensitive data is given additional protections and is prohibited unless authorized by law. International transfer of personal information is prohibited to countries without adequate protection. Individuals have an express right to access information about themselves held by government or private entities. The bill sets up an independent commission within the Ministry of Justice to enforce the law. The U.S. Direct Marketing Association launched a lobbying effort against the bill in December 1998 urging Argentinean companies to oppose the efforts to enact the law.

Under the Code of Penal Procedure, "A judge may arrange, for the purposes of building a case, the intervention of telephone communications or whatever other means of communication" [237]. The Civil Code does not mention electronic communications, nor does the Penal Code provide penalties for such privacy violations.

In November 1998, the City of Buenos Aires approved a law on access to information. The law gives all persons the right to ask for and to receive information held by the local authorities and the right of judicial review of data held in databases. Individuals have the right under *habeas data* to update, rectify, make confidential, or suppress information [238].

9.2. Brazil

Article 5 of the 1988 Constitution of Brazil provides, in part: "(10) The privacy, private life, honor, and image of persons are inviolable, and the right to compensation for property or moral damages resulting from the violation thereof is ensured; (11) The home is the inviolable asylum of the individual, and no one may enter it without the dweller's consent, save in the case of *in flagrante delicto* or disaster, or to give help, or, during the day, by court order; (12) The secrecy of correspondence and of telegraphic, data and telephone communications is inviolable, except, in the latter case, by court order, in the events and in the manner established by the law for purposes of criminal investigation or criminal procedural discovery; (14) Access to information is ensured to everyone and confidentiality of the source is protected whenever necessary for the professional activity" [239].

The Informatics Law of 1984 protects the confidentiality of stored, processed, and disclosed data, and the privacy and security of physical, legal, public, and private entities [240]. Citizens are entitled to access and correct their personal information recorded in private or public databases.

The 1990 Code of Consumer Protection and Defense [241] allows all consumers to "access any information derived from personal and consumer data stored in files, archives, registries, and databases, as well as to access their respective sources. Consumer files and data shall be objective, clear, true, and written in a manner easily understood, and shall not contain derogatory information for a period over five years. Whenever consumers find incorrect data and files concerning their person, they are entitled to require immediate correction, and the archivist shall communicate the due alterations to the incorrect information within five days. Consumer databases and registries, credit protection services, and similar institutions are considered entities of public nature. Once the consumer has settled his/her debts, Credit Protection Services shall not provide any information which may prevent or hinder further access to credit for this consumer." Brazil signed the American Convention on Human Rights on 25 September 1992.

A bill promoting the privacy of personal data in conformance with the OECD guidelines, to affect both public and private sector databases, was proposed in the Senate in 1996 and has yet to be voted on by the Federal Senate. The Bill provides that, "No personal data nor information shall be disclosed, communicated, or transmitted for purposes different than those that led to structuring such data registry or database, without express authorization of the owner, except in case of a court order, and for purposes of a criminal investigation or legal proceedings. It is forbidden to gather, register, archive, process, and transmit personal data referring to: ethnic origin, political or religious beliefs, physical or mental health, sexual life, police or penal records, family issues, except family relationship, civil status, and marriage system. Every citizen is entitled to, without any charge, access his/her personal data, stored in data registries or databases, and correct, supplement, or eliminate such data, and be informed by data registry or database managers of the existence of data regarding his/her person" [242].

On April 2001 the Constitution and Justice Committee of the Brazilian House of Representatives approved the Bill of Law No. 3173/97, which sets forth general provisions regarding public and private documents produced and recorded by electronic means, including its authenticity and their use as evidence in court.

On 26 March 2001 the Regional Council of Medicine of the State of São Paulo (CREMESP) published a number of ethics guidelines concerning healthcare-related websites. The guidelines consider any website that allows the purchase of medicine without prescription to be offensive to medical ethics. In order to protect the privacy of personal and health data of patients, the guidelines require website owners to inform users about the website's storage mechanisms and security, as well as to allow users to access their own files and cancel or update them.

The Brazilian government is working towards the implementation of a national health card, on which healthcare professionals would log patient information. As part of the endeavor, some institutions are seeking to use computerized patient records, though the drafting of standards to govern the technology utilized in such systems is just beginning [243]. As in many countries, defining a common set of data elements is often one of the initial steps in such a process and some institutions in Brazil have reportedly developed the first stages of the application.

9.3.   Canada

There is no explicit right to privacy in Canada's Constitution and Charter of Rights and Freedoms [244]. However, in interpreting Section 8 of the Charter, which grants the right to be secure against unreasonable search or seizure, Canada's courts have recognized an individual's right to a reasonable expectation of privacy.

Canada has been very active in the area of privacy, confidentiality and the regulation of health information. A Charter of Privacy Rights [245] was proposed to the Parliament in March 2000. The Charter would create a broad constitutional right of privacy for all Canadians in all spheres and prevail over acts of Parliament. Under the proposed bill, every individual would be given the right to privacy. This right would include, but not be limited to, personal privacy, which includes physical and psychological privacy; privacy of space, which includes freedom from surveillance; privacy of communication, which includes freedom from monitoring and interception; and privacy of information, which includes freedom from collection, use, and disclosure of their personal information by others. Any interference with an individual's privacy would be an infringement of the individuals right to privacy unless the interference is reasonably justified, and unless it is impossible or inappropriate to do so, the individual's informed consent has been obtained. A four-part test is proposed to determine if interferences are reasonably justified. The only permissible interferences would be: (1) where lawful; (2) where necessary to achieve a compelling societal interest that warrants limiting an individual's privacy; (3) where no other lesser measure will accomplish this objective; and (4) where both the importance of the objective and the beneficial effects of the interference outweigh the privacy loss.

In April 2000, the Federal Parliament approved Bill C-6, the Personal Information Protection and Electronic Documents Act [246]. The Act adopts the CSA International Privacy Code, now a national standard (CAN/CSA-Q830-96), into law for enterprises that process personal information "in the course of a commercial activity," and for federally regulated employers with respect to their employees. It does not apply to information collected for personal, journalistic, artistic, literary, or non-commercial purposes. The measure is significant not only because it addresses a wide spectrum of electronic commerce, but also because it speaks to the definition of "personal health information" and how such data are to be treated. In relevant part, it states that "personal health information," with respect to an individual, whether living or deceased, means:

- Information concerning the physical or mental health of the individual;

- Information concerning any health service provided to the individual;

- Information concerning the donation by the individual of any body part or any bodily substance of the individual or information derived from the testing or examination of a body part or bodily substance of the individual;

- Information that is collected in the course of providing health services to an individual; or

- Information that is collected incidentally to the provision of health services to the individual.

By contrast, "personal information" is much broader and is defined as "information about an identifiable individual, but does not include the name, title, or business address or telephone number of an employee of an organization." The law is rather comprehensive and deals with how various categories of information can be collected, used, and disclosed. In some situations, information can be collected, used, and disclosed without an individual's knowledge or consent so long as certain conditions are met. Record retention, the refusal of information access, and the resolution of disputes are all dealt with to some degree.

The law went into effect for companies that are under federal regulation, such as banks, telecommunications, transportation, and businesses that trade data interprovincially and internationally in January 2001, except with respect to medical records, which are exempted from the new law until 2002, although most medical records, however, fall under provincial jurisdiction. In three years, the Act will cover provincially regulated sectors unless the province enacts "substantially similar" laws, such as Quebéc's law. The scope of the act is still limited. Still missing is an adequate legal regime covering such things as video surveillance, physical privacy, biomedical privacy, drug and DNA testing, to mention a few.

The federal Privacy Act [247] provides individuals with a right of access to personal information held by the federal public sector. In addition, the Privacy Act contains provisions regulating the confidentiality, collection, correction, disclosure, retention, and use of personal information. Individuals may request records directly from the institution that has the custody of the information. The Act establishes a code of fair information practices that apply to government handling of personal records. However, its provisions can be ignored when another federal Act allows for the processing of personal information. Individuals can appeal to a federal court for review if access to their records is denied by an agency, but are not authorized to challenge the collection, use, or disclosure of information.

Both the Personal Information Protection and Electronic Documents Act and the Privacy Act are overseen by the independent Privacy Commissioner of Canada [248]. Under the Privacy Act, the Commissioner has the power to investigate, mediate, and make recommendations, but cannot issue binding orders. The Commissioner can initiate a Federal Court review in limited circumstances relating to denial of access to records. In May 2000, the Commissioner called for an update of the Federal Privacy Act and expressed concern about the misuse of the Social Insurance Number, health privacy, and the release of census records.

Privacy legislation covering government bodies exists in almost all provinces and territories [249]. In the province of Québec, the Charter of Rights specifically mentions the right to privacy and the law regulates the collection and use of personal information held by private sector businesses operating in the province of Québec [250]. This law sets rules for the collection, confidentiality, correction, disclosure, retention and use of personal information by these businesses. It also provides individuals with a right of access and correction. Nearly every province has some sort of oversight body, but their powers vary. Québec's "Commission d'accès à l'information" has broad powers over the public and private sectors.

The government of the Province of Ontario recently passed legislation facilitating electronic commerce [251]. Effective in October 2000, the law is careful not to override existing privacy protections and contains specific language mandating that it should not be construed to limit certain enumerated privacy-related laws, or limit other laws intended to "protect the privacy of individuals." The Information and Privacy Commissioner of British Columbia has also been very active in promoting privacy through his/her oversight powers of public bodies and public education efforts. A number of provinces are now looking into adopting privacy legislation based on the Personal Information Protection and Electronic Documents Act.

Canada's Criminal Code makes the unlawful interception of private communications a criminal offense. Other federal legislation also has provisions related to privacy. The Telecommunications Act has provisions to protect the privacy of individuals, including the regulation of unsolicited communications. Identity issues are currently under debate in Canada. There is great concern about the use of the Social Insurance Number (SIN) by the private sector and identity theft. A Parliamentary committee recommended in May 1999 that an Act setting out limitations on the use of the SIN be developed and that agencies' use of the SIN should be documented [252]. Human Resources Development Canada released its recommendations in November 1999 stating that the SIN should not become a national client identifier because of "severe privacy concerns" and costs. Québec considered creating a mandatory ID card but dropped the idea in 1998. In Toronto, a system to fingerprint all welfare recipients was dropped in March 1999 after the contractor was unable to create a working system. The Ontario government continues to discuss a smartcard system for all citizens to access government services.

The federal Access to Information Act [253] provides individuals with a right of access to information held by the federal public sector. The Act gives Canadians and other individuals and corporations present in Canada the right to apply for and obtain copies of federal government records. "Records" include letters, memos, reports, photographs, films, microforms, plans, drawings, diagrams, maps, sound and video recordings, and machine-readable or computer files. The Act is overseen by the Office of the Information Commissioner of Canada [254].

The Commissioner can investigate and issue recommendations but does not have power to issue binding orders. The Canadian Federal Court has ruled that government has an obligation to answer all access requests regardless of the perceived motives of the requesters. Similarly, the Commissioner must investigate all complaints even if the government seeks to block him from so doing on the grounds that the complaints are made for an improper purpose. Each of the provinces also has a Freedom of Information law

Since 1998, COACH - Canada's Health Informatics Association, has provided leadership and guidance in the areas of security, privacy, and confidentiality. In 2001, COACH's Security and Privacy Committee, a multidisciplinary team of practitioners and experts from across Canada, developed a set of far-reaching guidelines for the protection of health information [255]. This very detailed work builds on international experience and is intended as a resource to assist health organizations to protect the information with which they are entrusted. At this time it is probably the most comprehensive set of guidelines for the protection of health information ever assembled.

9.4. Chile

Article 19 of Chile's Constitution secures for all persons: "Respect and protection for public and private life, the honor of a person and his family. The inviolability of the home and of all forms of private communication. The home may be invaded and private communications and documents intercepted, opened, or inspected only in cases and manners determined by law" [256].

Recently, Chile became the first Latin American country to enact a data protection law, although there are many insufficiencies that will require corrections to harmonize the law with the OECD and European Union recommendations. Act No. 19628, titled "Law for the Protection of Private Life" [257] came into force on October 1999. The law has twenty-four articles, covering processing and use of personal data in the public and the private sector and the rights of individuals to access, correct, and request judicial control. The law contains a chapter dedicated to the use of financial, commercial and banking data, and specific rules addressing the use of information by government agencies. The law includes fines and damages for the unlawful denial of access and correction rights. Only databanks in the government must be registered. There is no data protection authority, and enforcement of the law is done individually by each affected person. The law does not contain restrictions on transfers to third countries. Chile signed the American Convention on Human Rights on August 20, 1990.

9.5. Colombia

The country does not have specific legislation regarding privacy of personal data but in 18 August 1999 the Congress of Colombia passed the Law 527 by which the access and use of electronic messages, electronic commerce, and digital signatures are defined and regulated [258]. The Law also establishes certification authorities and other pertinent dispositions. In September 2000 the Law 527 was partially regulated by the Presidential Decree 1747 [259]. The Decree introduces (Article 13) restrictions regarding storage of private encryption keys. Privacy issues regarding personal data were not considered

9.6. Mexico

Article 16 of the 1917 Mexican Constitution provides in part: "One's person, family, home, papers or possessions may not be molested, except by virtue of a written order by a proper authority, based on and motivated by legal proceedings. The administrative authority may make home visits only to certify compliance with sanitary and police rules; the presentation of books and papers indispensable to verify compliance with the fiscal laws may be required in compliance with the respective laws and the formalities proscribed for their inspection. Correspondence, under the protective circle of the mail, will be free from all inspection, and its violation will be punishable by law" [260].

On 29 May 29 2000, the long awaited amendments to the Civil and Commercial Codes that set the ground for electronic transactions in Mexico were finally published (Mexican E-Commerce Act). These amendments, that follow the UNCITRAL model law, entered into force next June 7 [261]. The enactment amended the Federal Civil Code, the Federal Commercial Code, the Federal Civil Procedures Code, and the Federal Consumers' Protection Law. It covers consumer protection, privacy and digital signatures and electronic documents. It includes a new article in the Federal Consumer Protection Act giving authority to the government "to provide for the effective protection of the consumer in electronic transactions or concluded by any other means, and the adequate use of the data provided by the consumer" (Art. 1.VIII); and also to coordinate the use of Code of Ethics by providers including the principles of this law.

The law also creates a new chapter in the Consumer Law titled: "Rights of Consumers in electronic transactions and transactions by any other means." The new article 76 now provides, "This article will be applied to the relation between providers and consumers in transactions effectuated by electronics means. The following principles must be observed: I. Providers shall use information provided by consumers in a confidential manner, and shall not be able to transfer it to third parties, unless there is express consent from the consumer or a requirement from a public authority ... II. Providers must use technical measures to provide security and confidentiality to the information submitted by the consumer, and notify the consumer, before the transaction, of the characteristics of the system ... VI. Providers must respect consumer decisions not to receive commercial solicitations ..."

Mexico is a member of the Organization for Economic Cooperation and Development, but does not appear to have adopted the OECD Guidelines on the Protection of Privacy and Transborder Flows of Personal Data. Mexico has signed the American Convention on Human Rights.

9.7. Peru

The 1993 Constitution [262] sets out extensive privacy, data protection and freedom of information rights. Article 2 states: "Every person has the right: (1) To solicit information that one needs without disclosing the reason, and to receive that information from any public entity within the period specified by law, at a reasonable cost. Information that affects personal intimacy and that is expressly excluded by law or for reasons of national security is not subject to disclosure. Secret bank information or tax information can be accessed by judicial order, the National Prosecutor, or a Congressional investigative commission, in accordance with law and only insofar as it relates to a case under investigation. (2) To be assured that information services, whether computerized or not, public or private, do not provide information that affects personal and family intimacy. (3) To honor and good reputation, to personal and family intimacy, both as to voice and image. Every person affected by untrue or inexact statements or aggrieved by any medium of social communication has the right to free, immediate and proportional rectification, without prejudice to responsibilities imposed by law. (4) To secrecy and the inviolability of communications and private documents. Communications, telecommunications or instruments of communication, may be opened, seized, intercepted or inspected only under judicial authorization and with the protections specified by law. All matters unconnected with the fact that motivates the examination are to be guarded from disclosure. Private documents obtained in violation of this precept have no legal effect. Books, ledgers, and accounting and administrative documents are subject to inspection or investigation by the competent authority in conformity with law. Actions taken in this respect may not include withdrawal or seizure, except by judicial order."

A Data Protection Bill was introduced in Parliament in October 1999 [263]. The bill is based on the new Spanish Data Protection Act, the Italian Data Privacy Act, the Privacy Act of 1988 of Australia, the U.S. Restatement of Torts and the EU Data Protection Directive. The bill proposes the creation of a Data Protection Commissioner. When approved, the bill will make Peru fully compatible with the EU Directive legal system.

The Article 154 of the Penal Code states that "a person who violates personal or family privacy, whether by watching, listening to or recording an act, a word, a piece of writing or an image using technical instruments or processes and other means, shall be punished with imprisonment for not more than two years". Article 151 of the Penal Code states "that a person who unlawfully opens a letter, document, telegram, radiotelegram, telephone message or other document of a similar nature that is not addressed to him, or unlawfully takes possession of any such document even if it is open, shall be liable to imprisonment of not more than 2 years and to 60 to 90 days' fine".

The Organic Law of the National Identification Registry and Civil Society (1995) created an autonomous agency which may "collaborate with the exercise of the functions of pertinent political and judicial authorities in order to identify persons" but is "vigilant regarding restrictions with respect to the privacy and identity of the person" and "guarantees the privacy of data relative to the persons who are registered." The Law also requires all persons to carry a National Identity Document featuring a corresponding number, photograph and fingerprint [264]. The court must provide all personal data kept on file at the Public Registry upon request within 15 days [265]. In July 2000, a computer crimes act was enacted. Freedom of information is constitutionally protected under the right of *habeas data*.

Peru signed the American Convention on Human Rights in 1978 but withdrew from the jurisdiction of the American Court of Human Rights in July 1999.

9.8.   United States of America

There is no explicit right to privacy in the U.S. Constitution. The Supreme Court has ruled that there is a limited constitutional right of privacy based on a number of provisions in the Bill of Rights. This includes a right to privacy from government surveillance into an area where a person has a "reasonable expectation of privacy" [266] and also in matters relating to marriage, procreation, contraception, family relationships, child rearing and education. However, records held by third parties, such as financial records or telephone calling records, are generally not protected unless a legislature has enacted a specific law. The Court has also recognized a right of anonymity [267] and the right of political groups to prevent disclosure of their members' names to government agencies [268]. In January 2000, the Supreme Court heard Reno v. Condon, a case addressing the constitutionality of the Drivers Privacy Protection Act (DPPA), a 1994 law that protects drivers' records held by state motor vehicle agencies. In a unanimous decision, the Court found that the information was "an article of commerce" and can be regulated by the federal government [269].

The Privacy Act of 1974 protects records held by U.S. Government agencies and requires agencies to apply basic fair information practices [270]. Its effectiveness, however, is significantly weakened by administrative interpretations of a provision allowing for disclosure of personal information for a "routine use" compatible with the purpose for which the information was originally collected. Limits on the use of the Social Security Number have also been undercut in recent years for a number of purposes. There is no independent privacy oversight agency in the U.S. The Office of Management and Budget plays a limited role in setting policy for federal agencies under the Privacy Act, but it has not been particularly active or effective.

The Federal Trade Commission took an increasing interest in privacy issues during 1997 and the first part of 1998, particularly with regard to the Internet and electronic trade. In July 1998, it issued a call for legislation for the protection of data relating to children collected over the Internet and a recommendation regarding adult privacy that if self-regulation had not improved by the end of the year then a legislative approach should also be taken there. The first part of 1998 saw White

House policy on data protection and privacy move further forward and, in July of the same year, Vice President Gore announced a series of steps in the direction of an Electronic Bill of Rights. The Bill included support for regulation in the areas of medical and financial data, identity theft, children's privacy, and industry self-regulation with effective enforcement mechanisms in other areas.

An office within the Office of Management and Budget to coordinate federal stances towards privacy was created in early 1999, and a Chief Counselor for Privacy was appointed. The Counselor has only a limited advisory capacity, and most privacy advocates believe the position is ineffective in promoting privacy within the government. The Federal Trade Commission (FTC) has oversight and enforcement powers for the laws protecting children's online privacy, consumer credit information and fair trading practices but has no general authority to enforce privacy rights [271]. The FTC has received thousands of complaints but has issued opinions in only a few cases. It has also organized a series of workshops and surveys, which have found that industry protection of privacy on the Internet is poor, but the FTC had long said that the industry should have more time to make self-regulation work. In a shift from this historical position, the FTC has more recently recommended to the U.S. Congress that legislation is necessary to protect consumer privacy on the Internet due to the dismal findings in a survey of online privacy policy [272].

The U.S. has no comprehensive privacy protection law for the private sector. A patchwork of federal laws covers some specific categories of personal information. These include financial records, credit reports, video rentals, cable television, children's online activities, educational records, motor vehicle registrations, and telephone records. However other activities such as the selling of medical records and bank records, monitoring of workers, and video surveillance of individuals are currently not prohibited under federal law. There is also a variety of sectoral legislation on the state level that may give additional protections to citizens of individual states [273]. The tort of privacy was first adopted in 1905 and all but two of the 50 states recognize a civil right of action for invasion of privacy in their laws.

The Freedom of Information Act was enacted in 1966 and has been amended several times [274]. It allows for access to federal government records by any requestor, except those held by the courts or the White House. However, there are numerous exceptions, long delays at many agencies, and little oversight unless a requestor files a lawsuit to enforce his or her rights. It was amended in 1996 by the Electronic Freedom of Information Act to specifically provide access to records in electronic form [275]. There are also laws in all states on providing access to government records.

There has been significant debate in the United States in recent years about the development of privacy laws covering the private sector. The White House and the private sector maintain that self-regulation is sufficient and that no new laws should be enacted except for a limited measure on medical information. There are currently efforts in Congress to improve financial privacy by prohibiting banks from selling personal information of customers without permission, but the proposal is strongly opposed by the banking industry. There is substantial activity in the states, particularly in California, New York and Minnesota. In Massachusetts and Hawaii comprehensive privacy bills for the private sector are now under consideration.

Internet privacy has been a major issue. A series of companies, including Intel and Microsoft, were discovered to have released products that secretly track the activities of Internet users. Users have filed lawsuits under the wiretap and computer crime laws. In several cases, TRUSTe, an industry-sponsored self-regulation watchdog group ruled that the practices did not violate its privacy seal program. Significant controversy arose around online profiling, the practice of advertising companies to track Internet users and compile dossiers on them in order to target banner advertisements. The largest of these advertisers, DoubleClick, set off widespread public outrage when it began attaching personal information from a marketing firm it purchased to the estimated 100 million previously anonymous profiles it had collected. In July 2000 the Federal Trade Commission reached an agreement with the Network Advertisers Initiative, a group consisting of the largest online advertisers including DoubleClick, which will allow for online profiling and any future merger of such databases to occur with only the opt-out consent. The Childrens' Online Privacy Protection Act (COPPA), passed by Congress in 1998 and requiring parental consent before information is collected from children under the age of 13, went into effect in April 2000 [276].

In late December 2000, the U.S. Department of Health and Human Services (DHHS) released the long-awaited rules regarding the privacy and confidentiality of personal health information, referred to as "individually identifiable health information" [277]. The rules implement the privacy requirements of the Administrative Simplification segment of the Health Insurance Portability and Accountability Act of 1996 (HIPAA) and became effective in February 26, 2001. It includes standards to protect the privacy of individually identifiable health information and applies to health plans, healthcare clearinghouses, and certain healthcare providers engaged in certain electronic transactions. The use of the standards is expected to improve the efficiency and effectiveness of public and private health programs and healthcare services by providing enhanced protections for individually identifiable health information. These protections will begin to address growing public concerns that advances in electronic technology and evolution in the healthcare industry are resulting, or may result, in a substantial erosion of the privacy surrounding individually identifiable health information maintained by healthcare providers, health plans and their administrative contractors.

Disclosure of information without a patient's consent is permitted for certain law enforcement purposes, such as: compliance with court orders, subpoenas and warrants; mandatory reporting of certain wounds or injuries; notification of law enforcement of the commission of a crime, or death, that may have been the result of criminal conduct; and compliance with a law enforcement request for information associated with identifying a suspect or fugitive relating to a crime.

The privacy rules are based on a set of guiding principles regarding how medical information should be treated. The principles are:

- **Control** - persons should have the right to control how their personal medical information is used. This supports the provisions relating to patient consent for certain information disclosures, the right of patients to view and correct medical information, having the ability to obtain a covered entity's disclosure policy, and a patient's right to secure a disclosure history relating to their information.

- **Accountability** - those that hold, or exercise control over, a person's medical information can be held accountable for rule violations. Sanctions can be criminal, civil, or both, depending upon the particular circumstances involved.

- **Boundaries** - persons should have their health information used only for health purposes and not for some other unrelated matter unless their consent is obtained first. Additionally, if it is necessary to disclose medical information, only the minimum amount considered necessary ought to be disclosed.

- **Public Responsibility** - the rules appear to strike a balance between an individual's right to protect his/her medical information and the public need for certain information relating to the protection of public health, medical research, and other worthwhile endeavors. The final rules address some of these aspects so that legitimate public purposes can still be pursued.

- **Security** - those who hold and store private medical information must do so in a manner that maintains both the integrity and confidentiality of the information itself. Part of this effort may involve a privacy officer to oversee the development and implementation of policies and procedures consistent with the security requirements.

The "electronic transactions" to which the rules refer include various types of information transmitted electronically, such as healthcare claims, payments, eligibility information, and coordination of benefits information. Additionally, the rules govern all forms of individually identifiable health information, including oral communications and written records. This is particularly important in view of the growing use of public networks to access medical record repositories [278, 279].

Where the previous draft rules covered only electronic records, the final rules have been broadened to encompass all oral, written and electronic health information. The rules are over 1,500 pages in length; some important aspects are summarized below:

- **Limited Disclosure** - the use and disclosure of individually identifiable health information for purposes of treatment, payment, or routine healthcare operations are to be kept to the minimum necessary. Healthcare providers are given discretion in determining what health information is needed when sending medical records to other providers for purposes of medical treatment.

- **Patient Consent** - healthcare providers are to secure a patient's consent for the use, or disclosure of, medical information for routine matters such as treatment, payment and other public health purposes. Non-routine matters, such as healthcare marketing or insurance underwriting, require specific authorizations by patients that are specific and time-limited. In general, individually identifiable health information is not to be used for non-health purposes without patient consent.

- **Employer Limits** - employers sponsoring health plans covered by the Employee Retirement Income Security Act (ERISA) are required to separate the use of health information for medical purposes from employment purposes dealing with, for example, promotions and hiring. In a practical sense, such employers will be obligated to separate information used for the two different purposes, and will likely necessitate the use of a computer firewall between the two.

- **Patient's Right To Information** - patients will have the right to access their medical information as well as correct errors therein. Additionally, they can obtain a copy of their records disclosure history as well as be provided advance notice of a "covered entity's" policy governing the disclosure of protected health information.

- **Penalties** - violations of the new rule carry significant penalties, both criminal and civil. Civil penalties of up to

$25,000 per year and criminal penalties of $50,000/one year in prison to $250,000/ten years in prison are provided for. Criminal penalties are possible when the violations are knowing or intentional. The most severe sanctions are focused on instances where violations arise from the sale, transfer or use of protected information for personal gain, commercial advantage or malicious harm.

- **Security of Information** - covered entities having personal health information are obligated to protect its integrity and confidentiality, and are to take measures to avoid misuses and disclosures, both inadvertent and deliberate. Covered entities are also directed to have "privacy officers" to oversee and monitor an entity's policies and training.

- **Business Associates** - the final rule uses the term "business associate" rather that "business partner" to permit a covered entity to disclose protected health information to a business associate so long as the covered entity has secured written assurances that the associate will appropriately safeguard the information. A wide range of business associate relationships are possible, as such a relationship can arise when the covered entity discloses protected information to a third party for the purpose of performing a function on behalf of, or for providing services for, the covered entity. Excepted from the requirement for a written agreement, however, are disclosures made by a covered entity to health providers concerning healthcare treatment. In this respect, written disclosure agreements are apparently not necessary between a hospital and its physician medical staff.

- **Compliance Date** - many covered entities will have until 26 months after the effective date of the rule to comply with the new mandates. Based on the calculation of 26 months, most institutions will need to be in compliance by the early portion of 2003, depending upon final action taken by the present (G.W. Bush) administration.

- **Enforcement and Preemption** - the rules provide for the Department of Health and Human Services (DHHS) Office of Civil Rights to coordinate enforcement of these provisions. The new rules do not, however, preempt state laws that may be more strict. As a result, covered entities will need to be mindful of, and take into consideration, the privacy and confidentiality laws of other laws that are more stringent than the new rules.

Another set of rules [280], proposed in 1998 and still under discussion, is directed to the implementation of standards for the security of individual health information and electronic signature use by health plans, healthcare clearinghouses, and healthcare providers. The health plans, healthcare clearinghouses, and healthcare providers would use the security standards to develop and maintain the security of all electronic individual health information. The electronic signature standard is applicable only with respect to use with the specific transactions defined in the Health Insurance Portability and Accountability Act of 1996, and when it has been determined that an electronic signature must be used.

Implementation of the privacy requirements of the Administrative Simplification segment of the Health Insurance Portability and Accountability Act of 1996 (HIPAA) rules will be complex and there are many issues still being debated [281]. A comprehensive review of best principles for the implementation of privacy policies for the health sector has been recently published [282].

The U.S. Department of Commerce and the European Commission in June 2000 announced that they had reached an agreement on the Safe Harbor negotiations that would allow U.S. companies to continue to receive data from Europe. The European Parliament adopted a resolution in early July seeking greater privacy protections from the arrangement [283]. The Commission announced that it was going to continue with the agreement without changes.

The European Commission has adopted a Decision determining that an arrangement put in place by the U.S. Department of Commerce known as the "safe harbor" provides adequate protection for personal data transferred from the EU. At the same time, the Commission has adopted similar Decisions concerning Switzerland and Hungary. The purpose of the Agreement is to head-off the possibility that data transfers to the U.S. might be blocked following the entry into force in 1998 of the EU Data Protection Directive, which provides that personal data can only be transferred to third countries providing "adequate protection". Under the "safe harbor" U.S. companies can voluntarily adhere to a set of data protection principles recognized by the Commission as providing adequate protection and thus meet the requirements of the Directive as regards transfers of data out of the EU. Although participation in the "safe harbor" is optional, its rules are binding for those U.S. companies that decide to join, and compliance with the rules is backed up by the law enforcement powers of the Federal Trade Commission and, for airlines, by the U.S. Department of Transportation.

Data transfers to U.S. organizations that choose to remain outside the "safe harbor" will still be possible, but will either need to benefit from one of the allowed exceptions, e.g., where the individuals concerned have given their agreement, or will require alternative safeguards such as a contract. EU data exporters wishing to check whether their intended U.S. recipient enjoy "safe harbor" status will be able to refer to a publicly-available list maintained by the Department of Commerce or by somebody it designates for that purpose.

U.S. organizations that self-certify their adherence to the "Safe Harbor" Privacy Principles and publicly declare their commitment to it, will appear on the list, provided that they are subject to the jurisdiction of either the FTC or the Department of Transportation. They may lose their "safe harbor" benefits, and this will be made clear in the list, if they persistently fail to comply with the Principles. In many cases, individuals will also have the option of taking U.S. organizations to court in the U.S., under a "misrepresentation" statute – there would be misrepresentation if a company announced a certain privacy policy and then did not respect it – or under a specific statute such as the Fair Credit Reporting Act, which covers a number of situations where financial loss might occur, e.g., refusal of a loan.

The U.S. is a member of the Organization for Economic Cooperation and Development but has not implemented the OECD Guidelines on the Protection of Privacy and Transborder Flows of

Personal Data in many sectors, including the financial sector and the medical sector. The U.S. companies that signed the OECD Guidelines in 1981 do not appear to have kept their promises to enforce fair information practices once the threat of legislation faded in the early 1980s and many actively lobby against privacy laws.

10. Review of Regulatory Responses: National Initiatives in the Middle East and Africa

10.1. Israel

Section 7 of The Basic Law: Human Dignity and Freedom states that "(a) All persons have the right to privacy and to intimacy. (b) There shall be no entry into the private premises of a person who has not consented thereto. (c) No search shall be conducted on the private premises or body of a person or in the body or belongings of a person. (d) There shall be no violation of the secrecy of the spoken utterances, writings or records of a person" [284].

The Protection of Privacy Law regulates the processing of personal information in computer data banks [285]. The law set out eleven types of activities that violated the law and could subject violators to criminal or civil penalties. Holders of data banks of over 10,000 names must register. Information in the database is limited to purposes for which it was intended and must provide access to the subject. There are broad exceptions for police and security services. It also sets up basic privacy laws relating to surveillance, publication of photographs and other traditional privacy features. The law was amended in 1996 to broaden the databases covered such as those used for direct marketing purposes, and also increased penalties.

The Act is enforced by the Registrar of Databases within the Ministry of Justice. The Registrar maintains the register of databases and can deny registration if he believes that a database is used for illegal activities. The registrar can also investigate and enforce the Act. A public council for the protection of privacy has also been set up to advise the Justice Minister on legislative matters related to the Protection of Privacy Law and its subsidiary regulations and orders. The council sets guidelines for the protection of computerized databases and guides the Registrar of Databases in his/her work.

Interception of communications is governed by the Secret Monitoring Law of 1979, which was amended in 1995 to tighten procedures and to cover new technologies such as cellular phones and e-mail. Unauthorized access to computers is punished by the 1995 Computer Law [286]. The Postal and Telegraph Censor, which operates as a civil department within the Ministry of Defense, has the power to open any postal letter or package to prevent harm to state security or public order.

The 1996 Patient Rights Law imposes a duty of confidentiality on all medical personnel [287]. The Supreme Court ruled that there was a fundamental right for citizens to obtain information from the government [288]. The Freedom of Information Law was approved unanimously by the Knesset in May 1998. It provides for broad access to records held by government offices, local councils and government-owned corporations. Requests for information must be processed within thirty days. A court can review decisions to withheld information.

10.2. South Africa

Section 14 of the South African Constitution of 1996 states: "Everyone has the right to privacy, which includes the right not to have – (a) their person or home searched; (b) their property searched; (c) their possessions seized; or (d) the privacy of their communications infringed." Section 32 states: "(1) Everyone has the right of access to – (a) any information held by the state; and (b) any information that is held by another person and that is required for the exercise or protection of any rights; (2) National legislation must be enacted to give effect to this right, and may provide for reasonable measures to alleviate the administrative and financial burden on the state".

The provisional Constitution contained an provision essentially similar to Section 14, in Section 13 [289]. The South African Constitutional Court has delivered a number of judgments on the right to privacy relating to the scope of privacy in society. All the judgments were delivered under the provisions of the Interim Constitution as the causes of action arose prior to the enactment of the Final Constitution. However, as there is no substantive difference between the privacy provisions in the Interim and Final Constitutions, the principles remain authoritative for future application.

The Access to Information Act was approved in February 2000 [290]. The bill covers both public and private sector entities and allows for access, rights of correction and limitations on disclosure of information. Originally introduced as the Open Democracy Bill, the proposed legislation also included comprehensive data protection provisions. However, those provisions were removed by the Parliamentary Committee in November 1999. The Committee wrote that it would be dealing with the right to privacy in Section 14 of the Constitution in an *ad hoc* and undesirable manner and that the intention is that South Africa, in following the international trend, should enact separate privacy legislation. The Committee, therefore, requested the Minister for Justice and Constitutional Development to introduce Privacy and Data Protection legislation, after thorough research on the matter, as soon as reasonably possible. The Privacy and Data Protection Bill is still in its early stages of development.

South Africa does not have a privacy commission but has a Human Rights Commission which was established under Chapter 9 of the Constitution and whose mandate is to investigate infringements on and to protect the fundamental rights guaranteed in the Bill of Rights, and to take steps to secure appropriate redress where human rights have been violated. The Commission has limited powers to enforce the Access to Information Act. There are no other specific pieces of legislation on general data protection law. Other than the Constitutional right to privacy, the South African common law protects rights of personality under the broad umbrella of the *actio injuriarum*. The elements of liability for an action based on invasion of privacy are the same as any other injury to the personality, namely an unlawful and intentional interference with another's right to seclusion and to private life. The Law Commission is currently drafting a new computer crimes law.

The Cabinet approved a plan in March 1998 to issue a multi-purpose smartcard that combines access to all government departments and services with banking facilities. This is part of the information technology strategy formulated by the Department of Communications to provide kiosks for access to government services.

In the long term, the smartcard is intended to function as passport, driver's license, identity document, and bankcards.

11. Review of Regulatory Responses: National Initiatives in Asia

11.1. Australia

The Australian Federal Constitution and the Constitutions of the six Australian States do not contain any express provisions relating to privacy. The principal federal statute is the Privacy Act of 1988 [293]. The Privacy Act gave effect to Australia's agreement to implement in the public sector the guidelines adopted in 1980 by the Organization for Economic Cooperation and Development (OECD) for the Protection of Privacy and Transborder Flows of Personal Data, as well as to its obligations under Article 17 of the International Covenant on Civil and Political Rights.

The Act defined a set of eleven Information Privacy Principles (IPPs), based on those in the OECD Guidelines, which apply to the activities of most federal government agencies. A separate set of rules about the handling of consumer credit information, added to the law in 1989, applies to all private and public sector organizations. The third area of coverage is the use of the government issued Tax File Number (TFN), where the entire community is subject to Guidelines issued by the Privacy Commissioner, which take effect as subordinate legislation.

The Office of the Privacy Commissioner is a member of the Human Rights and Equal Opportunity Commission but with the functions vested in the office rather than in the Commission. The origins of the Privacy Act were the protests in the mid-1980s against the Australia Card scheme – a proposal for a universal national identity card and number. The controversial proposal was dropped, but use of the tax file number was enhanced to match income from different sources with the Privacy Act providing some safeguards. The use of the tax file number has been further extended by law to include benefits administration as well as taxation. Some controls over this matching activity were introduced in 1990.

The government examined the advisability of extending legislation on privacy to the private sector. In March 1997 the Prime Minister called upon Australian businesses to develop voluntary codes of conduct to meet privacy standards. Subsequently informal consultations with business and consumers were held and a consultation paper was issued that addressed options for the content and implementation of a national scheme for fair information practices in the private sector. The scheme attempted to provide a viable self-regulatory option but was designed to be compatible with existing Commonwealth privacy laws and any further legislation that might be considered necessary in particular sectors, States or Territories. In the broad consultations that followed, it quickly became clear that the major issue was the need for national consistency in privacy standards to avoid a patchwork of different standards applying across industries, technologies, and State and Territory boundaries.

It also became clear that, while there were contentious issues in relation to the content of the principles that would underlie a national scheme, issues around coverage, implementation, and compliance mechanisms would be even more difficult to resolve. The National Principles for the Fair Handling of Personal Information represent the first stage in the development of a national privacy scheme for Australia.

The Commission had the opportunity to provide informal comments on the principles to the Australian Privacy Commissioner. The Commonwealth Government carried out a nationwide consultation with a view to introducing a national privacy standard, on a purely voluntary basis. In parallel however, the State of Victoria, introduced privacy legislation covering both the public and private sector in the Spring 1998 session of Parliament. It is designed to be the default privacy legislation covering those sectors and companies that fail to develop appropriate self-regulatory initiatives.

After several policy reversals, the re-elected conservative government introduced legislation to extend privacy protection to the private sector in April 2000. The Privacy Amendment (Private Sector) Bill 2000 applies a set of National Privacy Principles developed by the Privacy Commissioner during 1997 and 1998, originally as a self-regulatory substitute for legislation. The National Principles impose a lower standard of protection in several areas than the EU Directive. For example, organizations are required to obtain consent from customers for secondary use of their personal information for marketing purposes where it is "practicable"; otherwise, they can initiate direct marketing contact, providing they give the individual the choice to opt out of further communications. Controls on the transfer of personal information overseas are also limited, requiring only that organizations take "reasonable steps" to ensure personal information will be protected, or "reasonably believes" that the information will be subject to similar protection as applied in the Australian law. Nevertheless, the Bill includes an innovative principle of anonymity. Principle 8 states that: "Wherever it is lawful and practicable, individuals must have the option of not identifying themselves when entering into transactions with an organization." The Privacy Amendment (Private Sector) Act 2000 was passed in December 2000 [294].

The Government has described the Bill as a "light touch legislative regime" which establishes a minimum standard of privacy protection which can be replaced by approved industry codes, which must meet at least the minimum standards in the National Principles. The Bill attracted controversy and widespread debate, with privacy and consumer groups and some business groups expressing concern at its failure to meet international standards of privacy protection.

Public sector privacy issues continue to raise concerns. As part of reforms to the Australian tax system from July 2000, the Australian Taxation Office (ATO) required all enterprises to obtain an Australian Business Number. The ATO collected registration details including address and e-mail account, and planned to make this available to the public through the Australian Business Register and through selling it to database companies. A storm of protest occurred in June 2000 when it was realized that the register would include the home address and other details of almost 2 million individuals, who were sole traders, contractors or even had just a minor income from a hobby or some other activity. The Government agreed to amend the legislation, limit the content of the Australian Business Register, and allow individuals to suppress their details. At the same time, the Government was forced into another defeat after receiving legal advice that the Australian Electoral Commission had illegally disclosed information on around 10 million registered Australian voters.

The Office of Privacy Commissioner [295] has a wide range of functions, including handling complaints, auditing compliance, promoting community awareness, and advising the government and others on privacy matters. The Commissioner's office, which was initially well funded, suffered major budget cutbacks in 1997, at the same time as the Commissioner's range of responsibilities under several laws and in response to government requests was expanding.

A mix of privacy standards applies to the telecommunications sector. The Telecommunications (Interception) Act of 1979 [296] regulates the interception of telecommunications. A warrant is required under the Act, which also provides for detailed monitoring and reporting. Part 13 of the Telecommunications Act of 1997 [297] contains a general prohibition on the disclosure of telecommunications-related personal information. However, this principle contains a detailed list of exceptions. The Interception Act safeguards also need to be read alongside Part 15 of the Telecommunications Act of 1997, which places obligations on telecommunications providers to provide an interception capability and to positively assist law enforcement agencies with interception.

The Crimes Act [298] also contains a range of other privacy related measures, such as offenses relating to unauthorized access to computers, unauthorized interception of mail and telecommunications and the unauthorized disclosure of Commonwealth government information.

During 2000, Commonwealth and State governments have announced plans to move towards unique patient identifiers in the health sector, likely to be centered on a health smartcard. Health services are primarily delivered by the public sector in Australia, with only around a third of the population having private health insurance. The responsibility for delivery of health services is shared between the Commonwealth Government, which is responsible for much of the funding of the health system, and the States, which operate hospitals and community health services. The Commonwealth's proposal, HealthConnect, is intended as a voluntary national health information network under which health-related information about an individual would be collected in a standard, electronic format at the point of care.

The Australian States and Territories have various privacy laws. The New South Wales Privacy and Personal Information Protection Act of 1998 recently came into effect. It is based on a set of OECD-style Information Protection Principles and requires all government departments and agencies to develop a Privacy Management Plan demonstrating their compliance plans. It also allows government agencies to weaken the Information Protection Principles that form the foundation of the legislation. In Victoria, an information privacy bill was introduced in May 2000. It covers the public sector with principles similar to the National Privacy Principles. The Australian Capital Territory (ACT) enacted a health privacy law in 1997, and the Queensland government has committed to implement the April 1998 recommendation of a Parliamentary Committee for a public sector privacy law.

The federal Freedom of Information Act of 1982 [299] provides for access to government records. The Commonwealth Ombudsman promotes the Act and handles complaints about procedural failures.

11.2. China

There is no general data protection law in China and few laws that limit government interference with privacy. There are limited rights to privacy in the Chinese Constitution. Article 37 provides that the "freedom of the person of citizens of the People's Republic of China is inviolable," and Article 40 states: "Freedom and privacy of correspondence of citizens of the People's Republic of China are protected by law. No organization or individual may, on any ground, infringe on citizens' freedom of privacy of correspondence, except in cases where to meet the needs of state security or of criminal investigation, public security or prosecutorial organs are permitted to censor correspondence in accordance with procedures prescribed by law" [300].

Concerns with the growing use of the Internet has led to technical and legal restrictions. With the assistance of American companies such as Bay Networks, China has developed a "Great Firewall" which limits traffic to the Internet outside China to only three gateways. The firewall also blocks some western news websites such as the BBC, New York Times and the Voice of America. In February

1999, the government announced the creation of the State Information Security Appraisal and Identification Management Committee which, according to the official Xinhua state news agency, "will be responsible for protecting government and commercial confidential files on the Internet, identifying any net user, and defining rights and responsibilities..." The move is intended to guard both individual and government users, protect information by monitoring, and keep information from being used without proper authorization.

Under Article 7 of the Computer Information Network and Internet Security, Protection and Management Regulations [301], "the freedom and privacy of network users is protected by law. No unit or individual may, in violation of these regulations, use the Internet to violate the freedom and privacy of network users," and Article 8 states that "units and individuals engaged in Internet business must accept the security supervision, inspection, and guidance of the public security organization. This includes providing to the public security organization information, materials and digital documents, and assisting the public security organization to discover and properly handle incidents involving law violations and criminal activities involving computer information networks." Articles 10 and 13 stipulate that Internet account holders must be registered with the public security organization and lending or transferring of accounts is strictly prohibited.

The secrecy of communications is cited in the constitution and in law, but apparently with little effect. In practice, authorities often monitor telephone conversations, fax transmissions, electronic mail, and Internet communications of foreign visitors, businessmen, diplomats, and journalists, as well as Chinese dissidents, activists, and others. The government has created special Internet police units to increase control over Internet content and access.

The Chinese government announced and then retracted a broad-sweeping rule that required all entities other than embassies to register any software using encryption or including encryption technology. The original rule was announced on 10 November 1999 by the People's Republic of China State Encryption Management Commission and required registration by January 31, 2000. However, after few companies registered by the due date, and under increasing pressure due to successful China's World Trade Organization bid, officials reversed the hugely unpopular law, which would have banned foreign encryption software.

The Practicing Physician Law requires that doctors not reveal health information obtained during treatment. Doctors who violate the law face criminal penalties. In May of 1999, the Ministry of Health, with the approval of the State Council, published an administrative order declaring that personal information about HIV/AIDS sufferers be kept secret, and that the legal rights and interests of those people and their relatives should not be infringed. The Ministry of Health order asked all units and individuals in charge of diagnosis, treatment, and management work not to publish any personal information about HIV/AIDS sufferers, such as the name and the family address.

Special Administrative Region of Hong Kong

Following the People's Republic of China's resumption of sovereignty over Hong Kong on 1 July 1997, the constitutional protections of privacy are contained in the Basic Law of the Hong Kong Special Administrative Region of the People's Republic of China. Article 29 provides "The homes and other premises of Hong Kong residents shall be inviolable. Arbitrary or unlawful search of, or intrusion into, a resident's home or other premises shall be prohibited." Article 30 provides, "The freedom and privacy of communications of Hong Kong residents shall be protected by law. No department or individual may, on any grounds, infringe upon the freedom and privacy of communications of residents except that the relevant authorities may inspect communications in accordance with legal procedures to meet the needs of public security or of investigation into criminal offenses." Also relevant is Article 17 of the International Covenant on Civil and Political Rights, which was incorporated into Hong Kong's domestic law with the enactment of the Bill of Rights Ordinance. Article 39 of the Basic Law provides that the Covenant as applied to Hong Kong shall remain in force and implemented through the laws of Hong Kong.

In 1995, Hong Kong enacted its Personal Data (Privacy) Ordinance, and most of its provisions took effect in December 1996. The legislation enacts most of the recommendations made by the Hong Kong Law Reform Commission following its six-year comparative study [302]. The statutory provisions adopted features of a variety of existing data protection laws and the draft version of the EU Directive is also reflected in several provisions. It sets six principles to regulate the collection, accuracy, use, and security of personal data as well as requiring data users to be open about data processing and conferring on data subjects the right to be provided a copy of their personal data and to effect corrections.

The Ordinance does not differentiate between the public and private sectors, although many of the exemptions will more readily apply to the former. A broad definition of "personal data" is adopted so as to encompass all readily retrievable data recorded in all media that relate to an identifiable individual. It does not attempt to differentiate personal data according to its sensitivity. The Ordinance imposes additional restrictions on certain processing, namely data matching, transborder data transfers, and direct marketing. Data matching requires the prior approval of the Privacy Commissioner. The transfer of data to other jurisdictions is subject to restrictions that mirror those of the EU Directive. Also based on the directive is the requirement that upon first use of personal data for direct marketing purposes, a data user must inform the data subject of the opportunity to opt out from further approaches. The Commissioner had informal discussions with the EU over the question of adequacy but has not received a formal note on the adequacy of the statute.

The Ordinance establishes the Office of the Privacy Commissioner to promote and enforce compliance with statutory requirements. The Commissioner is given strong enforcement powers based on those contained in the U.K. Data Protection Act. In addition to investigating complaints, the Commissioner may initiate his/her own investigations of reasonably suspected contraventions. He may also conduct audits of selected data users. A contravention of any provision other than a data protection principle is a criminal offense. A contravention causing the data subject damage (including injured feelings) is a basis for claiming compensation. The Commissioner is empowered to designate classes of data users required to publicly register the main features of their data processing. The Commissioner may issue codes of conduct to provide guidance on compliance with the Ordinance's necessarily general provisions.

The Code on Access to Information [303] requires civil servants to provide records held by government departments unless there are specific reasons for not doing so. Departments can withhold information if it relates to sixteen different categories including defense, external affairs, law enforcement and personal privacy. Formal complaints of denials can be filed with the Ombudsman.

11.3. India

The Constitution of India does not expressly recognize the right to privacy. However, the Supreme Court first recognized in 1964 that there is a right of privacy implicit in the Constitution under Article 21 of the Constitution, which states: "No person shall be deprived of his life or personal liberty except according to procedure established by law" [304].

There is no general data protection law in India. The National Task Force on Information Technology and Software Development [305], established by the Prime Minister's Office in May 1998, submitted an "IT Action Plan" in July 1998 calling for the creation of a "National Policy on Information Security, Privacy and Data Protection Act for handling of computerized data." It examined the U.K. Data Protection Act as a model and recommended a number of cyber laws including ones on privacy and encryption.

In May of 2000, the government passed the Information Technology Act, a set of laws intended to provide a comprehensive regulatory environment for electronic commerce [306]. Chapter III of the bill gives electronic records and digital signatures legal recognition, and Chapter X creates a Cyber Appellate Tribunal to oversee adjudication of cybercrimes such as damage to computer systems (Section 43) and breach of confidentiality (Section 72). After strong criticism, sections requiring cybercafes to record detailed information about users were dropped. The legislation gives broad discretion to government law enforcers through a number of provisions – Section 69 allows for interception of any computer resource and requires that users disclose encryption keys or face a jail sentence up to seven years. Section 80 allows deputy superintendents of police to conduct searches and seize suspects without a warrant; Section 44 imposes stiff penalties on anyone who fails to provide requested information to authorities; and

Section 67 imposes strict penalties for involvement in the publishing of materials deemed obscene in electronic form. There is also a right of privacy guaranteed by Indian laws. Unlawful attacks on the honor and reputation of a person can invite an action in tort and/or criminal law.

A draft Freedom of Information Act was introduced into the Parliament in July 2000 [307]. The bill would provide a general right to access information and create a National Council for Freedom of Information and State Councils. It contains seven broad categories of exemptions. The draft was heavily criticized by campaigners who said that the bill provided only limited access to government records.

11.4. Japan

Article 21 of the 1946 Constitution states: "Freedom of assembly and association as well as speech, press and all other forms of expression are guaranteed; and that no censorship shall be maintained, nor shall the secrecy of any means of communication be violated." Article 35 states: "The right of all persons to be secure in their homes, papers and effects against entries, searches and seizures shall not be impaired except upon warrant issued for adequate cause and particularly describing the place to be searched and things to be seized; and that each search or seizure shall be made upon separate warrant issued by a competent judicial officer" [308].

The 1988 Act for the Protection of Computer Processed Personal Data Held by Administrative Organs governs the use of personal information in computerized files held by government agencies [309]. It is based on the OECD guidelines and imposes duties of security, access, and correction. Agencies must limit their collection to relevant information and publish a public notice listing their files systems. Information collected for one purpose cannot be used for a purpose "other than the file holding purpose." The Act is overseen by the Government Information Systems Planning Division of the Management and Coordination Agency. The Japanese government has followed a policy of self-regulation for the private sector, especially relating to electronic commerce.

The Ministry of International Trade and Industry (MITI) has issued a set of personal data protection guidelines for the sectors under its responsibility [310]. Each sector was invited to draw up its guidelines. From April 1998, a privacy mark was introduced for those companies that implement the data protection guidelines, and a supervisory body was established with the responsibility of investigating noncompliance. The Japanese Information Processing Development Center (JIPDEC) developed the privacy mark following the Guidelines Concerning the Protection of Personal Data in Electronic Commerce in the Private Sector prepared by the MITI.

The development of the guidelines was mostly coordinated by the privacy committee of the Electronic Network Consortium (ENC), which is concerned with resolving fundamental issues of network management. It has investigated appropriate ways to protect and control personal data collected by Japanese online service providers, and it has prepared guidelines for protecting personal data in the Internet age. The committee is a trade organization run by the New Media Development Association, an auxiliary organization of the Ministry of International Trade and Industry. To date, ninety-two organizations are members of the ENC, including most of the major online service providers in Japan: corporate members in the areas of commercial online services and Internet service providers, computer manufacturers, and communications and related software businesses. There are also special individual members, including academic and research professionals and fifty-one local community organizations that are interested in public networking.

The guidelines clearly state that personal data may be collected only with the consent of the individuals concerned. They clarify the right to veto the use of personal data, so that personal data already available to an online service provider cannot be used or transferred to a third party without the consent of the individual concerned. To ensure the proper management of personal data, a manager within the organization who understands the objectives of the guidelines and who is capable of implementing them should be appointed to manage the personal data.

Several committees have been set up to develop legislation for the private sector. In July 1999, government set up the Working Party on Personal Data Protection under the Advanced Information and

Telecommunications Society Promotion Headquarters. In January 2000, the government convened the Expert Committee for Drafting Law of Personal Data Protection under the Advanced Information and Telecommunications Society Promotion Headquarters to develop a comprehensive basic law to protect personal information on the basis of the Interim Report of the Working Party. The panel released an interim report in June 2000 urging the adoption of legal protections for the processing of personal information by businesses and the creation of a government office to handle complaints and investigations. It also recommended changes to laws on information held by government agencies. The panel is scheduled to release its final report in September 2000 and the government will introduce a bill into Parliament in 2001 [311]. The Ministry of Finance and MITI announced plans to introduce legislation to protect individuals credit data in 2000 after a task force issues proposals.

The Law Concerning Access to Information Held by Administrative Organs was approved by the Diet in May 1999 after 20 years of debate [312]. The law allows any individual or company to request government information in electronic or printed form. A nine-person committee in the Office of the Prime Minister will receive complaints about information that the government refuses to make public and will examine whether the decisions made by the ministries and agencies were appropriate. Government officials will still have broad discretion to refuse requests but requestors will be able to appeal decisions to withhold documents to one of eight different district courts. The law goes into effect in 2001.

Japan is a member of the Organization for Economic Cooperation and Development and a signatory to the OECD Guidelines on Privacy and Transborder Dataflows.

11.5. South Korea

The Constitution provides for protection of privacy and secrecy of communications. Article 16 states: "All citizens are free from intrusion into their place of residence. In case of search or seizure in a residence, a warrant issued by a judge upon request of a prosecutor has to be presented." Article 17 states: "The privacy of no citizen may be infringed." Article 18 states: "The privacy of correspondence of no citizen shall be infringed" [313].

The Act on the Protection of Personal Information Managed by Public Agencies of 1994 sets rules for the management of computer-based personal information held by government agencies and is based on the OECD privacy guidelines [314]. Under the Act, government agencies must limit data collected, ensure their accuracy, keep a public register of files, ensure the security of the information, and limit its use to the purposes for which it was collected. The Act is enforced by the Minister of Government Administration.

Interest in promotion of electronic commerce has been a major impetus for recent developments. In May 1998 the Ministry of Commerce, Industry and Energy (MoCIE) proposed a set of guidelines for electronic commerce legislation, including protecting privacy in the digital trade environment. The Basic Act on Electronic Commerce was approved in January 1999. Chapter III of the Act requires that "electronic traders shall not use, nor provide to any third party, the personal information collected through electronic commerce beyond the alleged purpose for collection thereof without prior consent of the person of such information or except as specifically provided in any other law." Individuals also have rights of access, correction, and deletion, and data holders have a duty of security [315].

The Ministry of Information and Communication (MIC) set up a Cyber Privacy Center in April 2000 [316]. The Ministry issued guidelines in May 2000 on privacy. The guidelines require consent before collecting "sensitive information" such as political orientation, birthplace, and sexual orientation, and ISPs wishing to collect information about users under 14 must obtain parental consent. ISPs must display their privacy policies and establish security policies. The Ministry said it was planning to develop legislation in late 2000 that would incorporate the guidelines. A study by the Korea Information Security Agency in November 1999 found that most sites were collecting information but were lacking adequate privacy policies.

In 1997, the government proposed an "Electronic National Identification Card Project." The plan was based on a smartcard system and according to a local human rights group would "include universal ID card, driver's license, medical insurance card, national pension card, proof of residence, and a scanned fingerprint, among other things" [317].

The Act on Disclosure of Information by Public Agencies is a freedom of information act that allows Koreans to demand access to government records. It was enacted in 1996 and went into effect in 1998. The Supreme Court ruled in 1989 that there is a constitutional right to information "as an aspect of the right of freedom of expression, and specific implementing legislation to define the contours of the right was not a prerequisite to its enforcement."

South Korea is a member of the Organization for Economic Cooperation and Development and has adopted the OECD Guidelines on the Protection of Privacy and Transborder Flows of Personal Data.

11.6. Malasya

The Constitution of Malaysia does not specifically recognize the right to privacy [318]. The Ministry of Energy, Communications and Multimedia is drafting a Personal Data Protection Act that will create legal protections for personal data as part of the "National Electronic Commerce Master Plan". The purpose of the Bill is to ensure secrecy and integrity in the collection, processing, and utilization of data transmitted through the electronic network. The Ministry is looking at the OECD Guidelines, EU Data Directive, and the U.K., Hong Kong, and New Zealand legislation as models for the act. The bill has been delayed for several years as the Ministry has watched international developments such as the U.S./EU Safe Harbor negotiations. The government appears to be moving towards embracing a mix of self-regulation and government intervention.

In 1998, the Parliament approved the Communications and Multimedia Act, which has several sections on telecommunications privacy. Section 234 prohibits unlawful interception of communications. Section 249 sets rules for searches of computers and includes access to encryption keys. Section 252 authorizes police to intercept communications without a warrant if a public prosecutor considers that a communication is likely to contain information that is relevant to an investigation [319].

Several other laws relating to technology were approved in 1997, including The Digital Signature Act [320, 321] and the Computer Crime Act [322]. Section 8 of the Computer Crime Act allows police to inspect and seize computing equipment of suspects without a warrant or any notice. The suspect is also required to turn over all encryption keys for any encrypted data on his/her equipment. The act also outlaws eavesdropping, tampering with or falsifying data, sabotage through computer viruses or worms, among a host of cybercrimes. The Energy, Communications and Multimedia Ministry announced in July 2000 that it is developing a National Policy Framework on Information Security to provide guidelines on computer security.

11.7. New Zealand

Article 21 of the New Zealand Bill of Rights Act of 1990 states: "Everyone has the right to be secure against unreasonable search or seizure, whether of the person, property, or correspondence or otherwise" and the Human Rights Act 1994 prohibits discrimination.

New Zealand's Privacy Act was enacted in 1993 [323] and has been amended several times [324, 325, 326, 327, 328, 329]. It regulates the collection, use and dissemination of personal information in both the public and private sectors. It also grants to individuals the right to have access to personal information held about them by any agency. The Privacy Act applies to "personal information," which is any information about an identifiable individual, whether automatically or manually processed. The news media are exempt from the Privacy Act in relation to their news activities.

The Act creates twelve Information Privacy Principles generally based on the 1980 OECD guidelines and the information privacy principles in Australia's Privacy Act 1988. In addition, the legislation includes a new principle that deals with the assignment and use of unique identifiers. The Information Privacy Principles can be individually or collectively replaced by enforceable codes of practice for particular sectors or classes of information. At present, there is only one complete sectoral code of practice in force, the Health Information Privacy Code 1994. There are several codes of practice that alter the application of single information privacy principles: the Superannuation Schemes Unique Identifier Code 1995, the EDS Information Privacy Code 1997, and the Justice Sector Unique Identifier Code 1998.

In addition to the information privacy principles, the legislation contains principles relating to information held on public registers; it sets out guidelines and procedures in respect to information matching programs run by government agencies, and it makes special provision for the sharing of law enforcement information among specialized agencies.

The Office of the Privacy Commissioner is an independent oversight authority that was created prior to the Privacy Act by the 1991 Privacy Commissioner Act [330]. The Privacy Commissioner oversees compliance with the Act, but does not function as a central data registration or notification authority. The Privacy Commissioner's principal powers and functions include promoting the objects of the Act, monitoring proposed legislation and government policies, dealing with complaints at first instance, approving and issuing codes of practice and authorizing special exemptions from the information privacy principles, and reviewing public sector information matching programs. Complaints by individuals are initially filed with the Privacy Commissioner who attempts to conciliate the matter. If conciliation fails, the Proceedings Commissioner or the complainant, if the Proceedings Commissioner is unwilling, can bring the matter before the Complaints Review Tribunal, which can issue decisions and award declaratory relief, issue restraining or remedial orders, and award special and general damages.

The Official Information Act of 1982 [331] and the Local Government Official Information and Meetings Act of 1987 [332] are freedom of information laws governing the public sector. There are significant interconnections between this freedom of information legislation and the Privacy Act in subject matter, administration, and jurisprudence, so much so that the three enactments may be viewed, in relation to access to information, as complementary components of one overall statutory scheme. Enforcement is supervised by the Office of the Ombudsman [333] which hears complaints under the Official

Information Act and the Local Government Official Information and Meetings Act.

New Zealand is a member of the Organization for Economic Cooperation and Development and has adopted the OECD Guidelines on the Protection of Privacy and Transborder Flows of Personal Data. New Zealand is one of six countries involved in a European Commission study of methods of assessing whether laws of "third countries" meet the provisions of the EU data protection directive.

11.8. Philippines

Article III of the 1987 Constitution protects the right of privacy. Section 2 states: "The right of the people to be secure in their persons, houses, papers, and effects against unreasonable searches and seizures of whatever nature and for any purpose shall be inviolable, and no search warrant or warrant of arrest shall issue except upon probable cause to be determined personally by the judge after examination under oath or affirmation of the complainant and the witnesses he may produce, and particularly describing the place to be searched and the persons or things to be seized." Section 3 states: "(1) The privacy of communication and correspondence shall be inviolable except upon lawful order of the court, or when public safety or order requires otherwise as prescribed by law. (2) Any evidence obtained in violation of this or the preceding section shall be inadmissible for any purpose in any proceeding." Section 7 states: "The right of the people to information on matters of public concern shall be recognized. Access to official records, and to documents and papers pertaining to official acts, transactions, or decisions, as well as to government research data used as basis for policy development, shall be afforded the citizen, subject to such limitations as may be provided by law" [334].

There is no general data protection law but there is a recognized right of privacy in civil law [335, 336]. The Civil Code also states that "every person shall respect the dignity, personality, privacy, and peace of mind of his neighbors and other persons," and punishes acts that violate privacy by private citizens, public officers, or employees of private companies. The Republic Act 8972, the Electronic Commerce Act of 2000 [337] in its Sections 8, 9, and 10 of the law, gives legal status to data messages, electronic writing, and digital signatures, making them admissible in court. Section 23 mandates a minimum fine and a prison term of six months to three years for unlawful and unauthorized access to computer systems, and extends the consumer act, RA7394, to transactions using data messages.

The Code of Conduct and Ethical Standards for Public Officials and Employees [338] mandates the disclosure of public transactions and guarantees access to official information, records or documents. Agencies must act on a request within fifteen working days from receipt of the request. Complaints against public officials and employees who fail to act on request can be filed with the Civil Service Commission or the Office of the Ombudsman.

11.9. Singapore

The Singapore Constitution is based on the British system and does not contain any explicit right to privacy [339]. The High Court has ruled that personal information may be protected from disclosure under a duty of confidences. There is no general data protection or privacy law and the government has been aggressive in using surveillance to promote social control and limit domestic opposition [340].

In September 1998, the National Internet Advisory Board released an industry-based self-regulatory "E-Commerce Code for the Protection of Personal Information and Communications of Consumers of Internet Commerce" [341]. The code encourages providers to ensure the confidentiality of business records and personal information of users, including details of usage or transactions, would prohibit the disclosure of personal information, and would require providers not to intercept communications unless required by law. The code would also limit collection and prohibit disclosure of personal information without informing the consumer and giving an option to stop the transfer, ensure accuracy of records, and provide a right to correct or delete data.

In July 1998, the Singapore government enacted three major bills concerning computer networks. They are the Computer Misuse (Amendment) Act [342], the Electronic Transactions Act, and the National Computer Board (Amendment) Act. The CMA prohibits the unauthorized interception of computer communications. The CMA also provides the police with additional powers of investigation. Under the amended Act, it is now an offense to refuse to assist the police in an investigation. Amendments also widened the provisions allowing the police lawful access to data and encrypted material in their investigations of offenses under the CMA as well as other offenses disclosed in the course of their investigations. Such power of access requires the consent of the Public Prosecutor. The Electronic Transactions Act imposes a duty of confidentiality on records obtained under the act and imposes a fine and jail sentence for disclosing those records without authorization. Police have broad powers to search any computer and to require disclosure of documents for an offense related to the act without a warrant [343].

The Ministry of Health announced in August 1999 that it was creating a central medical database. The database will hold all patients' records from all hospitals and clinics in Singapore and be available to government and private doctors.

11.10. Republic of China (Taiwan)

Article 12 of the 1994 Taiwanese Constitution states: "The people shall have freedom of privacy of correspondence" [344]. The Computer-Processed Personal Data Protection Law was enacted in August 1995 [345, 346]. The Act governs the collection and use of person-identifiable information by government agencies and many areas of the private sector. The Act requires that "The collection or utilization of personal data shall respect the rights and interests of the principal and such personal data shall be handled in accordance with the principles of honesty and credibility so as not to exceed the scope of the specific purpose." Individuals have a right of access and correction, the ability to request cessation of computerized processing and use, and the ability to request deletion of data. Data flows to countries without privacy laws can be prohibited. Damages can be assessed for violations. The Act also establishes separate principles for eight categories of private institutions: credit information organizations, hospitals, schools, telecommunication businesses, financial businesses, securities businesses, insurance businesses, mass media, and "other enterprises, organizations, or individuals designated by the Ministry of Justice and the central government authorities in charge of concerned end enterprises."

There is no single privacy oversight body to enforce the Act. The Ministry of Justice enforces the Act for government agencies. For the private sector, the relevant government agency for that sector enforces compliance. The 1996 Telecommunications Law states "Unauthorized third parties shall not receive, record, or use other illegal means to infringe upon the secrets of telecommunications enterprises and telecommunications messages. A telecommunications enterprise should take proper and necessary measures to protect its telecommunications security" [347].

In 1997, the Taiwanese government proposed a new national ID card called the "National Integrated Circuit (IC) Card." The plan called for a smartcard system with over 100 uses for the card, including ID, health insurance, driver's license, taxation and possibly small-value payments. There were hearings to evaluate privacy concerns after protests about the plan arose. The government dropped the plan and is now creating a paper-based card, which may include a fingerprint. A smartcard-based system just for health information, which will use the national ID number, is also being developed.

11.11. Thailand

Section 34 of the 1997 Constitution states: "A person's family rights, dignity, reputation or the right of privacy shall be protected. The assertion or circulation of a statement or picture in any manner whatsoever to the public, which violates or affects a person's family rights, dignity, reputation or the right of privacy, shall not be made except for the case which is beneficial to the public." Section 37 states: "Persons have the freedom to communication with one another by lawful means. Search, detention or exposure of lawful communication materials between and among persons, as well as actions by other means so as to snoop into the contents of the communications materials between and among persons, is prohibited unless it is done by virtue of the power vested in a provision of the law specifically for the purpose of maintaining national security or for the purpose of maintaining peace and order or good public morality." Section 58 states:

"A person shall have the right to get access to public information in possession of a State agency, State enterprise or local government organization, unless the disclosure of such information shall affect the security of the State, public safety or interests of other persons which shall be protected as provided by law" [348].

The National Information Technology Committee (NITC) approved plans in February 1998 for a series of information technology laws. Six sub-committees under the National Electronics and Computer Technology Centre (NECTEC) were set up to draft the following bills: E-Commerce Law, Electronic Data Interchange Law, Privacy Data Protection Law, Computer Crime Law, Electronics Digital Signature Law, Electronics Fund Transfer Law and Universal Access Law. All six bills were submitted to the Cabinet in January 2000. A combined electronic commerce and digital signature law was approved by the Cabinet in July 2000 and is expected to be approved by the Parliament this year. The rest of the bills, including the data protection act, are still awaiting Cabinet approval. The Association of Thai Computer Industry (ATCI) called on the government in May 2000 to adopt the data protection law to promote trust in e-commerce.

The Official Information Act was approved in 1997 [349]. The Act sets a code of information practices on personal information system run by state agencies. The agency must: ensure that the system is relevant to and necessary for the achievement of the objectives of the operation of the State agency; make efforts to collect information directly from the subject; publish material about its use in the Government Gazette; provide for an appropriate security system; notify such person if information is collected about him or her from a third party; not disclose personal information in its control to other State agencies or other persons without prior or immediate consent given in writing by the person except in limited circumstances; and provide rights of access, correction and deletion. The Official Information Commission, under the Office of the Prime Minister, oversees the Act [350].

In 1997, Thailand began issuing a new national ID card with a magnetic strip. The computer system will be linked with other government departments, including the Revenue Department, the Ministry of Foreign Affairs, the Ministry of Defense, and the Office of the Narcotics Control Board. The government also plans to link the system with other governments to allow holders to travel in Asian countries without the need for a passport, using only the new card.

The Official Information Act allows for citizens to obtain government information such as the result of a consideration or a decision that has a direct effect on a private individual, work-plan, project and annual expenditure estimates, and manuals or order relating to work procedure of State officials that affects the rights and duties of private individuals. Individuals can appeal denials to the Official Information Commission.

12. Global Harmonization Initiatives

The European Union Directive 95/46/EC of the European Parliament and of the Council of 24 October 1995 [33] represents the first comprehensive effort to implement an international harmonization privacy framework. As previously examined data protection rules in the EU not only regulate processing personal data in the EU Member States but also comprise provisions on the transfer of data to third countries (Articles 25 and 26 of the Directive 95/46/EC). The basic criterion is that Member States should permit transfer of personal data only when the third countries concerned ensure an appropriate level of protection. If an appropriate protection level cannot be ensured, and on the assumption that none of the exceptions envisaged would apply, Member States would prevent those transfers.

Although the EU countries and the U.S. share similar concerns about the impact of electronic networks on the information privacy, the EU has addressed these concerns in very different ways from the U.S. When the Transatlantic Business Dialogue (TABD) met in November 1997, both European and American participants recognized the threats to global commerce posed by privacy regimes that require conformity to a certain approach. It supported mutual recognition by governments of industry-led, market-driven privacy protection principles to ensure consumer trust in electronic commerce. It also suggested that national privacy protection allow for differences in privacy protection, based on national political systems and local cultures. The TABD urged the governments of both the U.S. and the EU to work together with industry to understand how market-driven, self-regulatory solutions provide protection of, and ensure the continuation of, transborder personal data flows [351].

Following the lead of the EU, most countries in Latin America, New Zealand, Canada, and the Asia-Pacific region have chosen the legislative path, as opposed to self-regulation, the model sponsored by the U.S. and Japan. The global trend has been toward the adoption of legislation type models – Australia, which initially preferred a self-regulating approach, has backed away from self-regulation and is now adopting the legislative model [352].

Regardless of the regulatory model that is implemented, the goal is to ensure the development, agreement, and application of a fair and predictable set of rules across countries and regions, and to reduce the complications of jurisdiction and applicable law.

12.1. Privacy in Electronic Transactions

Consumer confidence in online health transactions requires adequate security, respect for privacy, and protection from unfair, deceptive, and fraudulent conduct. Ultimately, what is important is that consumers must feel comfortable with how their personal information is used and their ability to control its use, whether through government intervention or industry self-regulation. A global economy depends on the free flow of information, and there is a need to balance the free flow of information appropriately with individuals' right to privacy in ways that do not sacrifice the benefits that electronic commerce promises.

Online Internet-based transactions present particularly serious questions regarding legal reparation if some aspect of the deal is found to be unsatisfactory. The global nature of interactive communication technologies complicates the issue because choice of law, jurisdiction, and liability rules vary significantly among countries, and may result in uncertainties about consumer rights and business obligations in cross-border transactions.

Even if issues of applicable law and jurisdiction could be adequately resolved, international private litigation over small-value Internet transactions generally does not make practical or economic sense. Other non-traditional forms of dispute resolution can be a practical way to provide consumers with fast, inexpensive, and effective remedies, and can reduce businesses' exposure to foreign litigation. For this reason, efforts have been made to promote collaborative efforts among the private sector and consumer groups to develop and implement fair and effective Alternative Dispute Resolution (ADR) mechanisms for online transactions as one means of promoting consumer confidence and participation in electronic transactions. Many organizations and stakeholders have expressed interest and support for ADR mechanisms, including the Organization for Economic Cooperation and Development (OECD), the Global Business Dialogue on Electronic Commerce, the Internet Law and Policy Forum, the Trans-Atlantic Business Dialogue, and the Trans-Atlantic Consumer Dialogue. To examine ADR issues and options, the U.S. Department of Commerce and the Federal Trade Commission held a workshop in June 2000 [353] to promote discussion among interested stakeholders on how ADR programs can foster consumer confidence without unduly burdening business.

12.2. Self-Regulated Harmonization

The U.S. approach to privacy protection attempts to balance individuals' privacy rights with the benefits associated with the free flow of information. To achieve this balance, the U.S. traditionally has relied on a mix of sector-specific legislation, regulation, private sector codes of conduct, and market forces. It is the view of the U.S. Government and industry that the global nature of the Internet and its decentralized nature limit the effectiveness of traditional government regulation. Also, it is asserted that the Internet's interactive capabilities allow consumers to register their views immediately and precisely, dramatically increasing the likelihood that the marketplace will find the optimal balance between data protection and freedom of information values [351, 354].

The U.S. approach to securing these protections relies on a combination of private sector self-regulatory initiatives, government enforcement of existing legal protections, and efforts to better inform consumers. Moreover, both the U.S. private sector and governments believe that they must share information and cooperate across borders to ensure that these efforts are effective in a global marketplace [354].

In response to the U.S. Administration's challenge, the Better Business Bureau's Online Division (BBBOnLine) worked with industry, consumer representatives, and governments and issued a code of conduct [355]. Businesses adhering to the code must disclose terms of sale, avoid unfair and deceptive advertising, register with the local Better Business Bureau, and meet other reliability standards in order to display a reliability seal. In addition, these businesses must commit to participate in ADR proceedings. The U.S. Administration sees the Better Business Bureau's online division, BBBOnLine and the BBBOnLine Reliability Program, as a model for voluntary actions that can promote consumer confidence in online transactions. Other important efforts are also underway in the U.S. – for example, the Electronic Commerce Consumer Protection Group [356], whose members include AOL, American Express, AT&T, Dell, IBM, Microsoft, Time Warner, and Visa, issued a code of conduct for online business in June 2000. This code is an important statement of best practices for web merchants, and it encourages merchants to participate in fair and effective dispute resolution mechanisms.

The U.S. Administration has, however, held the belief that the private sector must do far more to improve the level of privacy protection in the U.S. and directed the Secretary of Commerce and the Director of the Office of Management and Budget to work with private industry and privacy advocacy groups to encourage development and adoption of effective codes of conduct and/or technological solutions to privacy protection on the Internet. Since then, the U.S. Department of Commerce has been working with the private sector on ways to improve the effectiveness of codes of conduct, enhance public education on privacy issues, and further privacy protection through technology development.

The U.S. Federal Trade Commission [357] plays a central role in defining and enforcing policy. The Federal Trade Commission enforces a variety of federal antitrust and consumer protection laws. The Commission seeks to ensure that the nation's markets function competitively, and are vigorous, efficient, and free of undue restrictions. The Commission also works to enhance the smooth operation of the marketplace by eliminating acts or practices that are unfair or deceptive. In general, the Commission's efforts are directed toward stopping actions that threaten consumers' opportunities to exercise informed choice. Finally, the Commission undertakes economic analysis to support its law enforcement efforts and to contribute to the policy deliberations of the Congress, the Executive Branch, other independent agencies, and state and local governments when requested.

Consumer protection activities are carried out under the following four enforcement programs – Advertising Practices, Marketing

Practices, Financial Practices, and Enforcement – supported by Planning and Information, Consumer and Business Education, Economic and Consumer Policy Analysis, and Program Management.

- Advertising Practices Program - enforces the nation's "Truth-in-Advertising" laws. Whether advertisements appear on television or radio, in newspapers or magazines, or on the Internet, these laws require companies to tell the truth and to back up their claims with reliable, objective evidence.

- Marketing Practices Program - fights schemes that use high and low technology to defraud consumers. The program studies trends, brings law enforcement actions, conducts regulatory and policy review, and educates consumers in connection with deceptive practices that occur in the sale of consumer goods and services. The priorities of the program include Internet fraud, telemarketing fraud, telecommunications and new technologies, investment opportunity fraud, direct mail fraud, and warranties and contracts frauds.

- Financial Practices Program - promotes fairness and accuracy in the provision of financial services and in the use of financial information. Financial services, including credit and leasing, play important roles in the daily lives of most Americans, who use credit cards, take out loans, and lease major products. These services also present challenging consumer protection issues, such as protecting the privacy of sensitive online personal information.

- Enforcement Program - protects consumers from deception and fraud by stopping deceptive advertising and marketing practices that cause economic losses, ensures that companies ordered to stop deceptive practices do so, and ensures that consumers receive important information required by various laws and rules to help them make accurate comparisons and informed decisions.

- Planning and Information Program - The Planning and Information Program develops, analyzes, and supplies information in order to target law enforcement and educational efforts, measure the impact of mission activities, and allocate resources. The program is responsible for various projects and functions, including: Consumer Response Center, Consumer Sentinel, Identity Theft and Assumption Deterrence, International Coordination, and Operations.

- Consumer and Business Education Program - plans, develops, and implements proactive and creative mission-related campaigns targeted to both broad and segmented consumer and industry audiences. This effort encourages informed consumer choice and competitive business practices in the marketplace, and is viewed by the Commission as a cost-effective way to help minimize consumer injury and obtain compliance with the law.

- Program Management - responsible for the overall management of the Mission and the accomplishment of its goal and objectives. Senior managers provide direction to Mission staff and promote the efficiency and effectiveness of Mission programs by, among other things, managing strategic planning, allocating resources, monitoring and reviewing substantive initiatives, and managing human resources.

The Federal Trade Commission (FTC) and other U.S. agencies, working closely with industry and consumer advocates, has participated in the OECD's efforts to produce guidelines for consumer protection online [358].

Regarding privacy protection through self-regulation and example, the U.S. Government has called on industry to provide online privacy policies that articulate the manner in which a company collects, uses, and protects data, and the choices it offers consumers with regard to their personal information. Based on FTC surveys of commercial sites, sixty-two percent now post privacy policies compared to two percent in 1998. Businesses have increasingly hired privacy experts and made the protection of consumer information a priority. However, only twenty percent of the surveyed sites have policies that satisfy all the generally accepted fair information principles and special protections for sensitive information, and choice about how network advertisers use personal information continues to be a major issue.

New technologies are seen as a possible solution. The Platform for Privacy Protection (PPP), a standard developed by the World Wide Web Consortium that will enable users to express their privacy preferences through their browsers, is an example. In September of 2000, a Department of Commerce Workshop demonstrated this technology [359].

12.3. User-Driven Regulatory Harmonization

The best-protected consumer is an educated consumer. A variety of strategies have been proposed to enhance the capacity of stakeholders and users to develop and use interactive communication technologies. Even in developing countries the major limiting factor is educational level, as most applications are primarily text-based and designed for educated and literate audiences – e.g., in the U.S., a large segment of the population has great difficulty in understanding legal statements [360]. Users may require assistance ("intermediaries") to successfully use interactive communication applications and protect their privacy while online [7]. Strategies to address the issue of "user readiness" include components of health and technology literacy and ability to comprehend privacy issues [7], and the use of toolkits that assist end-users in the evaluation of the quality of health sites [361].

The U.S. Federal Trade Commission has used the Internet to alert consumers to the telltale signs of fraud, the importance of privacy in the information age and other critical consumer protection issues. More than 200 of their consumer and business publications are available on their website [362]. The FTC also provides resources for online marketers using a variety of approaches such as compliance guides, brochures, public addresses, web-based public service announcements, and workshops on issues of interest [357].

12.4. Special Areas Requiring Protection Through Legal Regulation

There are areas where highly sensitive information has prompted even those countries that promote self-regulation to progressively move toward legislative regulation. This strategy was found necessary to provide strong legal protection to privacy. Those areas include [354]:

- Children's Information – e.g., in 1999 the U.S. Government enacted the Children's Online Privacy Protection Act requiring sites aimed at children to get verifiable parental consent before they gather and use personal information received from children under thirteen. The FTC issued rules to implement this Act in April 2000.

- Medical Records - the privacy of medical data is particularly important and legislation is being drafted in the U.S. and other self-regulating countries to protect the privacy of individual health records. However, additional legislation also will be needed to ensure better protection of some medical records, such as those held by life insurance companies and in many employment uses that are outside the scope of the current statutes.

- Financial Records – users have been increasingly worried about the insufficient protection of privacy of financial records. In 2000, the U.S. Administration announced a new legislative proposal to protect consumers' financial privacy that includes the right to choose whether a firm shares consumer financial information, provides extra protection for especially sensitive information, and creates a new right to review and correct information collected about consumers. This proposal, developed by the Department of Treasury, the Office of Management and Budget and the National Economic Council, built upon the financial privacy protections of the 1999 Financial Modernization legislation and filled gaps in that ground-breaking law.

- Genetic Discrimination – in the U.S. on February 2000 a Presidential Executive Order banned the use of genetic information in Federal government hiring and promotion decisions. Legislation is still necessary to extend these protections to private sector employment and insurance practices.

12.5. Impact of the Diversity of Regulations at the International Level

Many nations share concerns about the impact of the expansion of electronic networks on information privacy. How to deal with privacy issues of transborder data flows has been a major issue between the European Union and the United States. Those conflicting perspectives are expected to expand to other countries due to globalized commerce and more and more countries, health organizations, and insurers becoming electronically integrated [363].

This situation could cause significant disturbances to flows of personal data throughout the world and, as a consequence, to international trade. The implications for countries such as the U.S., which receives a significant number of data transfers from the EU Member States and, in 1999, had approximately $350 billion in trade with the EU, are serious. Data transfers are the livelihood of many organizations and are the underpinnings for all of electronic commerce. Multinational organizations routinely share among their different offices a vast array of personal information. This information can be as simple as personnel telephone directories or can be more sensitive information such as personnel records, insurance information needed to process medical claims, credit card billing information, or patient information essential for conducting pharmaceutical research on new drugs. On the international front, the U.S. Government continues to promote an industry self-regulation approach to privacy protection with groups such the OECD, the Free Trade Area of the Americas (FTAA), and the Asia-Pacific Economic Cooperation. For example, the U.S. Government played a leading role in developing the OECD Online Privacy Generator, which encourages and helps organizations develop online privacy policies that comport with the 1980 OECD Privacy Guidelines. A very extensive review on the topic was recently published [364].

Although it is possible to prevent transfers of personal data by referring to Article XIV of the GATS (General Agreement on Trade in Services), it would be preferable to avoid resorting to this type of action [365]. A much more satisfactory solution would be that third countries toward which data are transferred set up a level of protection that could be considered as adequate and agreed upon by all parties.

With a view to establishing a predictable and workable framework ensuring high data protection standards and at the same time the free flow of personal data across the Atlantic, an informal dialogue on data protection between the European Union Commission's services and the U.S. Department of Commerce started in early 1998. During the year, the dialogue intensified: several high-level meetings took place. The Working Party and the Committee established by Article 31 of Directive 95/46/EC were regularly informed about progress. On November 1998, the U.S. Department of Commerce issued a set of privacy principles designed to offer a "safe harbor" to U.S. companies and organizations that adhere to them on a voluntary basis. Led by the U.S. Department of Commerce's International Trade Administration and the European Commission Directorate for Internal Markets, an agreement was reached with the goals of ensuring the free flow of data and effective protection of personal data between the U.S. and the E.U. and the establishment of a "safe harbor" framework, based on principles that more closely reflect the U.S. approach to privacy, which at the same time meet the European Directive's adequacy requirements. These principles were deemed adequate by the European Commission in July 2000. The safe harbor became effective on 1 November 2000 [366].

Private sector organizations such as the Global Business Dialogue on Electronic Commerce and the TransAtlantic Business Dialogue also help find ways to bridge different national privacy approaches. Moreover, in May 2000, BBBOnfine and the Japan Information Processing Development Center (JIPDEC) teamed up to develop a transnational online privacy seal. The seal can be displayed by businesses that have earned either the JIPDEC or the BBBOnline privacy seals.

Although the EU saw these principles as a positive development, it was felt that improvements and clarifications would be necessary before the principles could be judged as offering "adequate protection" as required by the Directive 95/46/EC [283].

12.6. Implications for e-Commerce and e-Health

One of the IT-related societal transformations with highest visibility is the emergence of e-Commerce. Starting to take off in 1995 business-to-consumer (B2C) and business-to-business (B2B) electronic commercial transactions have risen rapidly. Estimates suggest that in the U.S. alone, in the year 2000, B2C e-Commerce represented a market of more than US$ 60 billion and B2B more than US$ 184 billion. Although estimates vary, and the impact of the present downturn in the world economy is still not clear, by 2003 B2C is expected to reach between US$ 75 to 144 billion and B2B between US$ 634 billion and 3.9 trillion. Also, by 2003 about eighty percent of all B2B transactions could take place online [367].

Reports have estimated that the Internet-based e-Commerce average potential value may represent something in the order of 30% of the GDP of developed economies, ranging from 2% in the coal industry up to 40% in electronic components and financial services. The main impetus for this trend has been ascribed to the massive implementation of e-Commerce Web sites. Another modality of electronically-mediated transactions are the consumer-to-consumer (C2C), also known as peer-to-peer (P2P), exchanges – still a very limited market from the commercial viewpoint, and mainly represented by auctions, direct selling of goods, and non-financial exchange of products.

The conversion of government and public-domain information and applications to a digital format and the deployment of online government services available seven days a week, twenty-four hours a day, has been radically changing the bureaucratic nature of public services. An example is the U.S. Government FirstGov Internet site -- a portal that allows users to search more than 27 million Federal agencies

Web pages. The site uses a search engine capable of examining half a billion documents in fractions of a second, handles millions of searches every day, and provides linkage to the home pages of agencies and entities in all government branches.

Other public areas where e-Government applications have caused great impact are: record-keeping, legal and regulatory databases, online procurement, electronic form filling, social services applications and benefit distribution, student aid management, social security operation, legal counseling, submission of complaints, electronic payments, tax returns, and voting [367, 368, 369].

Those developments led to the emergence of "e-Health", as an area distinguished by: "the combined use of electronic communication and information technology in the health sector," or "the use in the health sector of digital data – transmitted, stored and retrieved electronically – for clinical, educational, and administrative purposes, both at the local site and at distance" [370, 371]. Most e-Health solutions build on the experience of e-Commerce and e-Government strategies in using networked technologies to rethink, redesign, and rework how businesses and public services operate.

In developed countries, e-Health has rapidly evolved from online medical content dissemination to the adaptation of generic e-commerce solutions in the processing of health-related administrative transactions and clinical care. Emerging new areas of health application are oriented toward professional networking, healthcare process management, and the provision of Web-based care – this expanded view has been promoted as the final stage in bringing the entire healthcare industry online [367].

Governments and private organizations must grapple with transnational and global e-Commerce and e-Health regulatory and legal issues and address them in a comprehensive and collaborative manner. Those issues are particularly worrisome due to the growing number of national, international and non-governmental actors involved in transnational and global healthcare [372]. Although progress has been successfully achieved in the European Union, the current organizational structure and "institutional culture" of the health sector in most countries are not conducive to interdisciplinary, rapid-response collaborative work, and the implementation of political and managerial tasks required to address such multifaceted complex problems.

On the positive side, concerns about the social, economic, national market impacts, and legal implications of the new technologies and networked global marketplaces have prompted the international community to address some most pressing crossborder issues involving data flow and privacy, at least at the level of declarations of intention.

Initiatives concerned with information and communication technologies and development that most recently addressed the issues of access, privacy, and crossborder impacts are: the Digital Opportunity Taskforce (DOT Force) established by the leaders of the G-8 countries at the Kyushu-Okinawa Summit [369, 373]; the Ministerial Declaration at the United Nations Economic and Social Council (ECOSOC) of 2000 [374]; the United Nations ICT Task Force [375]; the Florianópolis Declaration of 2000 by the representatives of Latin American and Caribbean countries [376]; the Brasília Communiqué of the Presidents of South America [377]; the Group of Fifteen Jakarta Declaration [378]; the Rio de Janeiro Declaration of the Intergovernmental Meeting on ICT for Development [379]; the 2001 Declaration of the Rio Group [380]; the Declaration of Santiago of the Rio Group and the European Union Minister's Meeting [381]; and the recommendations of the ECOSOC 2001 Council of July 2001 [382].

13. Internet Sources on Regulatory and Legal Issues on Data Security and Privacy

Set forth below are a number of different websites that offer valuable information pertaining to privacy, confidentiality, security, and medical or health records. Inclusion of website references should not, in any way, be construed as an endorsement of the sponsoring entity or agreement with all the information, views, positions or perspectives contained therein. Additionally, inclusion of website listings does not imply that all information contained on such sites is always accurate. Users are cautioned to remember that the Internet is a dynamic, quickly changing medium. Some information that was available at the original time it was accessed may become unavailable in the future. The authors of this publication made no distinctions regarding government, for-profit, not-for-profit, or commercial sites.

13.1. Key Resources

- American Health Information Management Association
  http://www.ahima.org/

- Alan S. Goldberg's Law, Technology & Change Home Page
  http://world.std.com/~goldberg/

- Baker & McKenzie, E-Commerce Law
  http://www.bmck.com/ecommerce/

- Center for Healthcare Information Management
  http://www.chim.org/

- Electronic Privacy Information Center
  http://www.epic.org/

- Electronic Commerce in Canada
  http://www.e-com.ic.gc.ca/english/privacy/regs.html

- Internet Healthcare Coalition
  http://www.ihealthcoalition.org/

- U.S. Dept. of Health & Human Services – Administrative
  Simplification
  http://aspe.os.dhhs.gov/admnsimp/

13.2. Other Resources

13.2.1. United States

- AAMC – Government Affairs & Advocacy
  http://www.aamc.org/advocacy/issues/research/confid.htm
  This site includes an issue brief on confidentiality of medical records
  and a link to congressional activity on the issue

- American Health Lawyers Association
  http://www.healthlawyers.org/home.htm

- American Bar Association, Committee on Cyberspace Law
  http://www.abanet.org/buslaw/cyber/initiatives/jurisdiction.html

- American Medical Informatics Association
  http://www.amia.org/

- American Medical Association
  http://www.ama-assn.org/med-sci/cpt/emr.htm
  This site has information on electronic medical records
  implementation and security issues, as well as AMA testimony on
  computer-based patient records.

- American Telemedicine Association
  http://www.atmeda.org/
  Association of companies and individuals interested in telemedicine
  and telehealth. Site offers industry news, legislative information, and
  position papers.

- California Telehealth & Telemedicine Center
  http://www.telehealth.calhealth.org/

- Chicago-Kent College of Law, Cyberlaw Jurisdiction
  http://www.kentlaw.edu/cyberlaw/

- Consolidation of Computer-based Patient Record Institute (CPRI) and Healthcare Open Systems and Trials (HOST)
  http://www.cpri.org/

- Duke Medical Informatics Home Page
  http://dmi-www.mc.duke.edu/

- e-Health Reports of the California HealthCare Foundation
  http://ehealth.chcf.org/

- Electronic Frontier Foundation (EFF)
  http://www.eff.org
  EFF is a non-profit, non-partisan organization working in the public interest to protect fundamental civil liberties, including privacy and freedom of expression in the arena of computers and the Internet .

- Electronic Healthcare Network Accreditation Commission
  http://www.ehnac.org/
  Accrediting body for electronic health information

- FindLaw
  http://www.findlaw.com/

- FirstGov
  http://www.firstgov.gov/
  Access to all U.S. government websites, including legislation, statutes, regulations, and agencies

- Georgetown University – Institute for Health Care Research & Policy, Health Privacy Project
  http://www.healthprivacy.org/
  Offers a variety of links and resources on health privacy, federal law and state law in the United States.

- HIPAAdvisory, The industry center for HIPAA and health information security & privacy.
  http://www.hipaadvisory.com/
  News, analyses, surveys, and databases regarding HIPAA-related information.

- Health Care Compliance Association
  http://www.hcca-info.org/index.html
  Non-profit association devoted to enhancing healthcare compliance

- The Informatics Review
  http://www.informatics-review.com/
  An e-journal of the Association of Medical Directors of Informations Systems

- Joint Healthcare Information Technology Alliance
  http://www.jhita.org/abtjhita.htm
  An alliance of several organizations focused on effectively using technology and offering important information on HIPAA, e-Health, telemedicine, and other areas.

- Medical Group Management Association (MGMA)
  http://www.mgma.com
  This site will have the MGMA's position on a number of issues facing healthcare, including confidentiality of patient records. It includes the ability to search the site for its postings on different issues (e.g., confidentiality)

- McBride, Baker & Coles
  http://www.mbc.com/
  Law firm site offering a variety of information, including privacy, confidentiality, medical records, HIPAA, and Internet-related materials.

- National Association of Boards of Pharmacy
  http://www.nabp.net/

- National Coalition for Patient Rights
  http://www.cciw.com/content/confidentiality.html
  The NCPR is a non-profit organization interested in patient's rights
  to privacy. This website assesses the impact of proposed
  healthcare legislation on these rights.

- National Conference of State Legislatures – Internet Sites of State
  Legislatures
  http://www.ncsl.org/public/sitesleg.htm
  Links to all the state legislatures, from which legislative, statutory
  and administrative regulation information can be obtained pertaining
  to selected states.

- National Council of State Boards of Nursing
  http://www.ncsbn.org/

- North Carolina Healthcare Information and Communications
  Alliance
  http://www.nchica.org/

- Office for the Advancement of Telehealth
  http://telehealth.hrsa.gov/
  U.S. Federal office aimed at fostering telemedicine and telehealth,
  which also contains valuable information and links relating to
  telemedicine, telehealth, electronic records, and other relevant
  topics.

- Risk Management Foundation of the Harvard Medical Institutions
  http://www.rmf.harvard.edu/publications/forum/v19n3/article2/index.
  html
  This site provides information on a forum for "Risk Management in
  the CyberAge" including confidentiality issues related to electronic
  medical records.

- Stanford Medical Informatics
  http://www-camis.stanford.edu/

- Thomas – Legislative Information on the Internet
  http://thomas.loc.gov/home/thomas2.html
  This site offers comprehensive access to a wide variety of federal
  legislative information, including recently enacted and pending
  Congressional bills, regulations, and committee reports.

- The National Academies – Institute of Medicine
  http://www.iom.edu/

- The National Academies - Computer Science and
  Telecommunications Board
  http://www4.nationalacademies.org/cpsma/cstb.nsf

- National Archives and Records Administration - Federal Register
  http://www.nara.gov/fedreg/

- Tech Law Journal
  http://www.techlawjournal.com/welcome.htm
  A site offering helpful legal information, including legislation, statutes
  and case law dealing with privacy, confidentiality, medical records
  and the Internet.

- Telemedicine Information Exchange
  http://tie.telemed.org/
  A site offering news, grant information, website links, and databases
  relevant to telemedicine and telehealth

- U.S. Dept. of Commerce – Safe Harbor
  http://www.export.gov/safeharbor/

- U.S. Department of Defense (DoD)
  http://www.dod-telemedicine.org/

- U.S. National Library of Medicine
  http://www.nlm.nih.gov/

- U.S. National Library of Medicine - National Telemedicine Initiative
  http://www.nlm.nih.gov/research/telemedinit.html
  Links to a variety of telemedicine and electronic health information-
  related sites, including programs, resources and symposiums.

- University of California-Berkeley Library, Health Sciences
  Information Service
  http://www.lib.berkeley.edu/HSIS/
  A collection of health, medicine, and Internet related websites and
  journals.

- Western Governors' Association – Health Passport Project
  http://www.westgov.org/wga/initiatives/hpp/default.htm
  An Official G-7 Global Health-care Data Card Pilot Project, aimed at
  fostering effective and integrated healthcare information.

13.2.2. International

- Communication and Information Industries (CII) Directorate
  http://www.dti.gov.uk/cii/cii/index.shtml

- European Union
  http://europa.eu.int/comm/internal market/en/index.htm#
  This is the website if the Internal Market Directorate of the European
  Commission, at which all relevant news on legislation in force and
  proposed in the areas of e-Commerce and data protection can be
  found.

- EUROPARL - The multilingual Web server of the European
  Parliament
  http://www.europarl.eu.int/home/default_en.htm

- Council of Europe – Data Protection Pages
  http://www.legal.coe.int/dataprotection/

- OECD – Information Society Page
  http://www.oecd.org/dsti/sti/it/

- The Association Internationale de la Mutualité (AIM)
  http://www.aim-mutual.org/uk/index.htm
  AIM is a grouping of autonomous health insurance and social
  protection bodies operating according to the principles of solidarity
  and non-profit-making orientation – good source of information on
  latest EU litigation in the health domain.

- European Health Management Association
  http://www.ehma.org/index.html

- European Health Telematics Association
  http://www.ehtel.org/

- The European Consumers' Organisation
  http://www.beuc.org/

- The European Commission - Media, Information Society and Data
  Protection
  http://europa.eu.int/comm/internal_market/en/media/dataprot/news/
  safeharbor.htm

- The European Telematics Horizontal Observatory Service
  http://www.ethoseurope.org/

- Global Internet Liberty Campaign
  http://www.gilc.org/
  Worldwide group that monitors and advocates for policies relating to
  the Internet, privacy, cybercrime, etc.

- Health On The Net Foundation
  http://www.hon.ch/home.html
  A non-profit group sponsoring a wide variety of Internet-available
  materials, including journals, websites and databases

- Internet Law and Privacy Forum
  http://www.ilpf.org/
  Provides information from legal and technical experts from member
  companies, businesses, governments, intergovernmental
  organizations, academia, and from the private practice of law
  around the world.

- International Medical Informatics Association
  http://www.imia.org/

- International Society for Telemedicine
  http://www.isft.org/
  International society devoted to telemedicine and telehealth around
  the world, with a site offering relevant links, articles, information and
  conferences.

- Journal of Medical Internet Research
  http://www.jmir.org/index.htm
  International scientific peer-reviewed journal on all aspects of
  research, information and communication in the healthcare field
  using Internet and Intranet-related technologies.

- People for Internet Responsibility
  http://www.pfir.org/#info
  A global, ad hoc network of people concerned about the current and
  future operations, development, management, and regulation of the
  Internet, including privacy, confidentiality and other matters

- Privacy International
  http://www.privacyinternational.org/
  A human rights group examining actions taken by governments and
  corporations, including actions relating to ID cards, video
  surveillance, data matching, police information systems, and
  medical privacy.

- UNESCO - United Nations Educational, Scientific and Cultural
  Organization. Observatory of the Information Society.
  http://www.unesco.org/webworld/observatory/index.shtml

References

[1]   European Commission (1994). *Growth, Competitiveness, Employment - The Challenges and Ways Forward in to the 21st Century. White Paper.* Luxembourg, EC Publications Office, CM-82-94-529-EN-C Euro-OP, L-2985

[2]   De Maeseneer J, Beolchi L (Editors) (1995). *Telematics in Primary Care in Europe.* Studies in Health Technology and Informatics Volume 20. IOS Press/Ohmsha, Amsterdam, ISBN 90 5199 209 2

[3]   European Commission (1996*). TELMED - The Impact of Telematics on the Healthcare Sector in Europe. Final Report.* Prepared by The Tavistock Institute, the European Center for Work and Society, and the Fondazione per la Ricerca sulla Migrazione e sulla Integrazione della Technologie. EU Commission Directorate DG XIII, November 1996. Available at www.ehto.be/ht_projects/telmed2

[4]   Pan American Health Organization (1998). *Information Systems and Information Technology in Health – Challenges and Solutions for Latin America and the Caribbean.* Health Services Information Systems Program, Division of Health Systems and Services Development. Washington, DC. ISBN 92 75 12246 6

[5]   Rodrigues RJ (1996*). Information systems development and health sector reform.* In Proceedings of the Sixth National and Fourth International Conference on Information Technology and Community Health (ITCH96*).* Victoria, BC, Canada, November 3-6. pg 2-7

[6]   Sosa-ludicissa M, Oliveri N, Gamboa CA, Roberts J (Editors) (1997). *Internet, Telematics and Health.* Studies in Health Technology and Informatics Volume 36. PAHO/WHO and IMIA. IOS Press, ISBN 90 5199 289 0

[7]   U.S. Department of Health and Human Services (1999). *Wired for Health and Well-Being - The Emergence of Interactive Health Communication.* Eng TR, Gustafson DH (Editors), Science Panel on Interactive Communication and Health. Office of Public Health and Science. U.S. Printing Office, Washington, DC

[8]   Organization for Economic Cooperation and Development (1997). *Global Information Infrastructure - Global Information Society (GII-GIS): Policy requirements.* Committee for Information, Computer and Communications Policy Publication OCDE/GD(97)139, Paris

[9]   Council on Competitiveness (1993). *Competition Policy: Unlocking the National Information Infrastructure.* Washington, DC, December

[10]   Council on Competitiveness (1996). *Highway to Health: Transforming U.S. Health Care in the Information Age.* Washington, DC, March

[11]   Commonwealth Secretariat (1997). *Telecommunications for Development in the Commonwealth. Report of a Workshop Held in Malta 22-24 May, 1997.* Education Department, Human Resource Development Division, Commonwealth Secretariat, Marlborough House, London

[12]   National Science and Technology Council (1999). *Information Technology Frontiers for a New Millenium*. A Report by the Subcommittee on Computing, Information, and Communications R&D, Committee on Technology. Published by the Executive Office of the President of the United States. Washington, DC

[13]   Rodrigues RJ (2000). *Information systems: the key to evidence-based health practice*. Bull World Health Org 78(11): 1344-1351

[14]   Rodrigues RJ (2000). *Telemedicine and the Transformation of Healthcare Practice in the Information Age*. In: Speakers' Book of the ITU Telecom Americas 2000 Telecom Development Symposium, Session TDS.2, Rio de Janeiro April 10-15, 2000, pg 91-105

[15]   United Nations Educational, Scientific and Cultural Organization (1999). *Report of the Experts Meeting on Cyberspace Law, Monte-Carlo, Principality of Monaco, 29-30 September 1998*. Document CII/USP/ECY/99/01

[16]   McLellan F (1998). *"Like hunger, like thirst": patient, journals, and the internet*. Lancet 352: Suppl 2, Oct 1998. Document can be found online at the site: http://www.thelancet.com/newlancet/reg/supplements/vol352s2/body.article12.html

[17]   Kiley R (1998). *Consumer health information on the Internet*. J Royal Soc Med 91:202-203

[18]   Dyer KA (1999). *The internet as an untapped medium of medical Web-education: a physician's perspective*. The CyberMed Catalyst, Issue 1. Document can be found online at the site: http://www.amip.org/catalyst/cc_space.htm

[19]   Boulding M, Mack J (1998). *Promoting the Benefits of the Web:The Internet Healthcare Coalition*. Document can be found online at: http://www.ihealthcoallition.org/content/articles_1.html

[20]   Lehmann CU (1997). *Consumers and the Medical Internet*. Document can be found online at the site: http://www.ihealthcoalltion.org/content/MWM_present5a.html

[21]   Stanberry BA (1999). *Legal and ethical issues in European telemedicine*. European Telemedicine 1998/99, 20-25

[22]   Goodman KW (Editor) (1998). *Ethics, Computing and Medicine: Informatics and the Transformation of Health Care*. Cambridge University Press, ISBN 0 521 4690 5 8

[23]   Hodge Jr JG, Gostin LO, Jacobson PD (1999). *Legal issues concerning electronic health information: privacy, quality, and liability*. JAMA 282:1466-1471

[24]   Eysenbach G (1999). *Towards ethical guidelines for dealing with unsolicited patient emails and giving teleadvice in the absence of a pre-existing patient-physician relationship – systematic review and expert survey*. Journal of Medical Internet Research Issue 1/2000. Document can be found online at the site: http://www.symposion.com/jmir/2000/1/e1/index.htm

[25]   Rodrigues RJ (2000). *Ethical and legal issues in interactive health communications: a call for international cooperation (Editorial)*. Journal of Medical Internet Research 2 (1): March. Available online at: http://www.symposion.com/jmir/index.htm

[26]   Terry N (2000). *Legal pitfalls of cybermedicine*. Medical Ethics Winter 2000: 4-7

[27]   Schanz SJ (Editor) (1999). *1999 Compendium of Telemedicine Laws - Selected Statute Excerpts and Article Citations Relating to Telemedicine.* Published by Legamed, Inc, Raleigh, NC. ISBN 0 965 7439 2 6

[28]   United Kingdom National Health Service (2001).*The Caldicott Report.* Published by The Department of Health. Available online at: http://www.doh.gov.uk/nhsexipu/confiden/report/index.htm

[29]   U.S. Department of Health and Human Services (1999). *Proposed Standards for Privacy of Individually Identifiable Health Information.* Document can be found online at the site: http://aspe.hhs.gov/admnsimp/pvcsumm.htm

[30]   European Commission Group on Ethics in Science and New Technologies (1999*). Ethical Issues of Healthcare in the Information Society.* Report # 13, Prof. Ina Wagner (Rapporteur) July 30, 1999. Document can be found online at the site: http://europa.eu.int/comm/secretariat_general/sgc/ethics/en/opinion13.pdf

[31]   IITF (1995). *Privacy and the NII: Safeguarding Telecommunications-Related Personal Information.* Report of the Information Infrastructure Task Force (IITF). National Telecommunications and Information Agency, U.S. Department of Commerce, Washington, DC, October

[32]   Institute of Medicine (1994). *Health data in the Information Age: Use, Disclosure, and Privacy.* Donaldson MD and. Lohr KN (Editors.). Washington, DC, National Academy Press

[33]   European Union (1995). *Directive 95/46/EC of the European Parliament and of the Council of 24 October 1995 on the protection of individuals with regard to the processing of personal data and on the free movement of such data.* Document can be found online at the site: http://www.europa.eu.int/comm/internal_market/en/dataprot/law/index.htm

[34]   Walker P (1998). *Status of Data Protection in the United Kingdom.* Document can be found online at the site: http://www.ehto.org/

[35]   Laske C (1996). *Legal issues in medical informatics: a bird's eye view.* In: Barber B, Treacher A, Louwerse K (Editors). *Towards Security in Medical Informatics: Legal and Ethical Aspects.* ISO Press, Oxford

[36]   Pernice A, Doare H, Rienhoff O (1995). *Healthcare Card Systems: Eurocards Concerted Action, Results and Recommendations.* Studies in Health Technology and Informatics Volume 22. IOS Press; Amsterdam. ISBN 90 519999 225 4

[37]   Laires MF, Ladeira MJ, Christensen JP (Editors) (1995*). Health Care in the New Communications Age: Health Care Telematics for the 21st Century.* Studies in Health Technology and Informatics Volume 24. IOS Press/Ohmsha, Amsterdam, ISBN 90 5199 224 6

[38]   Healthcare Informatics (1999). *2000 Resource Guide.* Healthcare Informatics, December: 17-176. McGraw-Hill; Minneapolis MN

[39]   Middleton B, Miller G (1999). *Protecting the Privacy and Confidentiality of the Internet Health Record.* MedicaLogic, Inc.; Hillsboro, OR

[40]   Bauer JC, Ringel MA (1999). *Telemedicine and the Reinvention of Healthcare.* Healthcare Informatics Executive Management Series. McGraw-Hill. ISBN 0 07134630 9

[41]   European Health Telematics Association (2001). *Study On The Use Of Advanced Telecommunications Services By Health Care Establishments And Possible Implications For Telecommunications Regulatory Policy Of The European Union.* Available online at: http://www.ehtel.org/, click the "publications" button and then select the article

[42]   Mendel B (1999). *Online identity crisis.* Infoworld October 18, 36-37

[43]   European Union (2000). *Directive 2000/31/EC on Electronic Commerce.* Available online at: http://europa.eu.int/eur-lex/en/lif/dat/2000/en_300L0031.html

[44]   Culnan MJ (1999). *Privacy and the Top 100 Web Sites: Report to the Federal Trade Commission.* The McDonough School of Business, Georgetown University, Washington, DC Document can be found online at the site: http://www.msb.edu/faculty/culnanm/GIPPS/oparpt.pdf

[45]   California HealthCare Foundation and the Internet Healthcare Coalition (2000). *Ethics Survey of Consumer Attitudes about Health Web Sites.* A report conducted by Cyber Dialogue in cooperation with the Institute for the Future. EHealth Reports January

[46]   Goldman J, Hudson Z, Smith RM (2000). *Privacy: Report on the Privacy Policies and Practices of Health Web Sites.* A California HealthCare Foundation preliminary report to the eHealth Summit Meeting, February 1-2, 2000, Washington, DC EHealth Reports January

[47]   Uxbridge Magistrates' Court (2000). *The History of Justices of the Peace (Magistrates).* Uxbridge Magistrates' Court, The Court House, Harefield Road, Uxbridge, Middlesex. UB8 1PQ U.K. Available online at: http://www.olmcs-law.co.uk/magistrates.html

[48]   United Nations (1948). *Universal Declaration of Human Rights.* Adopted and proclaimed by General Assembly resolution 217 A (III) of 10 December 1948. Available online at: http://www.un.org/Overview/rights.html

[49]   Organization of the American States (1965). O.A.S. Res XXX, Adopted by the Ninth Conference of American States. OEA /Ser L./V/I.4 Rev

[50]   Privacy International (2001). *Privacy and Human Rights: An International Survey of Privacy Laws and Practice.* An Internet site dedicated to the promotion of privacy and human rights. Available online at: http://www.gilc.org/privacy/survey/

[51]   U.S. Department of Health and Human Services (1999). *Proposed Standards for Privacy of Individually Identifiable Health Information.* Document can be found online at the site: http://aspe.hhs.gov/admnsimp/pvcsumm.htm

[52]   United Kingdom General Medical Council (1995). *Confidentiality: Guidance from the General Medical Council.* GMC, London

[53]   Beauchamp TL, Childress JF (1994). *Principles of Biomedical Ethics.* 4th Edition, Oxford University Press, New York

[54]   Flaherty D (19890. *Protecting Privacy in Surveillance Societies.* University of North Carolina Press; Raleigh, NC

[55]   Council of Europe (1981). *Convention for the Protection of Individuals with Regard to the Automatic Processing of Personal Data.* Convention ETS No. 108, Strasbourg. Available online at: http://www.coe.fr/eng/legaltxt/108e.htm

[56]   Organization for Economic Cooperation and Development (1980). *Guidelines
         Governing the Protection of Privacy and Transborder Data Flows of Personal
         Data.* Adopted by the Council 23 September 1980. Available online at:
         http://europa.eu.int/comm/internal_market/en/media/dataprot/inter/priv.htm or
         http://www.oecd.org/dsti/sti/it/secur/prod/PRIV-EN.HTM

[57]   United Nations (1990). *Guidelines Concerning Computerized Personal Data Files.*
         Adopted by the General Assembly on 14 December 1990. Available online at:
         http://www.datenschutz-berlin.de/gesetze/internat/aen.htm

[58]   European Union (1997). *Directive 97/66/EC Concerning the Processing of
         Personal Data and the Protection of Privacy in the Telecommunications Sector* .
         Directive of the European Parliament and of the Council of 15 December 1997.
         Available online at: http://www.europa.eu.int/ISPO/infosoc/telecompolicy/en/Main-
         en.htm

[59]   European Commission (1998). *Opinion 1/98: Platform for Privacy Preferences
         (P3P) and the Open Profiling Standard (OPS).* Adopted by the Working Party on
         16 June 1998. Available online at:
         http://europa.eu.int/comm/internal_market/en/media/dataprot/wpdocs/wp11en.htm

[60]   Council of Europe (1997). *Recommendation No. R (97) 5 of the Committee of
         Ministers to Member States on the Protection of Medical Data.* Adopted by the
         Committee of Ministers on 13 February 1997at the 584th meeting of the Ministers'
         Deputies. Available online at: http://www.cm.coe.int/ta/rec/1997/97r5.html

[61]   European Union (2000). *Citizens Rights and New Technologies: a European
         Challenge.* Report of the European Group on Ethics in Science and New
         Technologies on the Charter on Fundamental Rights Related to Technological
         Innovation as Requested by President Prodi on February 3, 2000. Available online
         at: http://europa.eu.int/comm/secretariat_general/sgc/ethics/en/prodi_en.pdf

[62]   European Economic Community (1993). *Council Directive 93/42/EEC of 14 June
         1993 Concerning Medical Devices.* Amended by 398L0079 (OJ L 331 07.12.1998
         p.1) and by 300L0070 (OJ L 313 13.12.2000 p.22). Available online at:
         http://europa.eu.int/eur-lex/en/lif/dat/1993/en_393L0042.html

[63]   European Economic Community (1985). *Council Directive 85/374/EEC of 25 July
         1985 on the Approximation of the Laws, Regulations and Administrative
         Provisions of the Member States Concerning Liability for Defective Products.*
         Incorporated by 294A0103(52) (OJ L 001 03.01.1994 p.263) and by
         294A0103(53) (OJ L 001 03.01.1994 p.321) and amended by 399L0034 (OJ L
         141 04.06.1999 p.20). Available online at: http://europa.eu.int/eur-
         lex/en/lif/dat/1985/en_385L0374.html

[64]   European Commission (2000). *Privacy on the Internet: An integrated EU
         Approach to On-line Data Protection.* Working Party on Data Protection and
         Privacy. Internal Market DG, Unit Doc 5063/00/EN/FINAL WP 37, adopted on 21
         November 2000. Available online at:
         http://europa.eu.int/comm/internal_market/en/media/dataprot/wpdocs/wp37en.pdf

[65]   European Commission (2001). *Opinion 1/2001 on the Draft Commission Decision
         on Standard Contractual Clauses for the transfer of Personal Data to third
         countries under Article 26(4) of Directive 95/46.* Draft distributed to the Working
         Party on 17 January 2001 and adopted on 26 January 2001. Available online at:
         http://europa.eu.int/comm/internal_market/en/media/dataprot/wpdocs/wp38en.htm

[66]   Blanke J (2001). *"Safe Harbor" and the European Union's directive on data
         protection.* Albany Law J Sci & Tech 57(1): 57

[67] Federal Republic of Austria (2001). *Datenschutzgesetz DSG, BGBl 1978/565 changed by 1981/314, 1982/228, 1986/370, 1987/605, 1988/233, 1989/609, 1993/91, 1994/79, 1994/632*. Österreichische Gesellschaft für Datenschutz (Austrian Society for Privacy and Data Protection). Available online at: http://www.ad.or.at/office/recht/dsg.htm

[68] Federal Republic of Austria (2001*). Datenschutzgesetz 2000, BGBl I Nr. 1999/165*. Österreichische Gesellschaft für Datenschutz (Austrian Society for Privacy and Data Protection). Available online at: http://www.ad.or.at/office/recht/dsg2000.htm

[69] Kingdom of Belgium (2001). *Constitution of Belgium*. Available online (English language version) at: http://www.fed-parl.be/constitution_uk.html

[70] Kingdom of Belgium (1998). *Projet de loi modifiant la loi du 8 décembre 1992 relative à la protection de la vie privée à l'égard du traitement des données à caractère personnel, no. 1586/1* (Rapporteur : M. Renaat Landuyt). Projet de loi transposant la Directive 95/46/CE du 24 octobre 1995 du Parlement européen et du Conseil relative à la protection des personnes physiques à l'égard du traitement des données à caractère personnel et à la libre circulation de ces données, no. 1566/1

[71] Kingdom of Belgium (1994). *Loi de 30 juin 1994 relative à la protection de la vie privée contre les écoutes, la prise de connaissance et l'enregistrement de communications et de télécommunications privées*

[72] Kingdom of Denmark (1953). *Constitution*. Available online at: http://www.uni-wuerzburg.de/law/da00t_.html

[73] Kingdom of Denmark (1978). *Lov nr 293 af 8 juni 1978 om private registre mv* (Private Registers Act of 1978), in force 1 January 1979

[74] Kingdom of Denmark (1978). *Lov nr 294 af 8 juni 1978 om offentlige myndigheders registre* (Public Authorities Registers Act of 1978), in force 1 January 1979

[75] Kingdom of Denmark (1998). *Behandling af personoplysninger* (Processing of personal data) Bet. 1345, 1997

[76] Kingdom of Denmark (1998). *Registertilsynet* (Data Protection Agency). Available online at: http://www.registertilsynet.dk/eng/index.html

[77] Madsen W (1992). *Handbook of Personal Data Protection*. London: Macmillan; New York: Stockton Press

[78] Republic of Finland (1999). *Constitution of Finland*. Available online at: http://www.om.fi/constitution/3340.htm

[79] Republic of Finland (1988). *Personal Data Files Act* (Law No. 471/87)

[80] Kuopus J (1994). *Data Protection Regulatory System, Data Transmission, and Privacy*. Campbell D, Fisher J (Editors). Netherlands: Martinus Nijhoff Publishers

[81] Empire of France (1858). *L' affaire Rachel. Judgment of June 16, 1858, Trib. pr. inst. de la Seine, 1858 D.P. III 62*. Cit. in Hauch JM (1994). Protecting Private Facts in France: The Warren & Brandeis Tort is Alive and Well and Flourishing in Paris. 68 Tul. L. Rev. 1219: May

[82] Republic of France (1978). *Loi no. 78-17 du Janvier 1978 relative à l'informatique, aux fichiers et aux libertés*. Journal officiel du 7 janvier 1978 et rectificatif au JO du 25 janvier 1978, modifiée par la loi no. 88-227 du 11 mars 1988, article 13 relative à la transparence financière de la vie politique (JO du 12 mars 1988), la loi no. 92-1336 du 16 décembre 1992 (JO du 23 décembre 1992) et la loi no. 94-548 du ler juillet 1994 (JO du 2 juillet 1994). Available online at: http://www.cnil.fr/textes/text02.htm

[83] Republic of France (1978). *Loi no. 78-753 du 17 juillet 1978 portant diverses mesures d'amélioration des relations entre l'administration et le public et diverses dispositions d'ordre administratif, social et fiscal*. Journal officiel du 18 juillet 1978, page 2851. Available online at: http://www.cnil.fr/textes/text05.htm

[84] Republic of France (1979). *Loi no. 79-18 du 3 janvier 1979 sur les archives*. Journal officiel du 5 janvier 1979, page 43, rectificatif au journal officiel du 6 janvier 1979, page 55. Available online at: http://www.cnil.fr/textes/text052.htm

[85] Web Site for the French National Commission for Informatics and Freedoms (2001). *Commission Nationale de l'Informatique et des Libertés* . Available online at: http://www.cnil.fr

[86] Federal Republic of Germany (1998). *Constitution.* Adopted on 23 May 1949 and last amended (46th Amendment) on 16 July 1998. Available online at: http://www.uni-wuerzburg.de/law/gm00000_.html

[87] Federal Republic of Germany (1977). *Federal Data Protection.* (Bundesgesetzblatt, Part I, No 7, 1 February 1977), Amended 20 December 1990. (BGBl.I 1990 S.2954 = Federal Law Gazette I, p. 2954), amended by law of September 14, 1994 (BGBl. I S. 2325 = Federal Law Gazette I, p. 2325), law of December 16, 1997 (BGBl. I S. 2325 = Federal Law Gazette I, p. 2325) and December 17, 1997 (BGBl. I S. 2325 = Federal Law Gazette I, p. 2325). Available online at: http://www.datenschutz-berlin.de/gesetze/bdsg/bdsgeng.htm

[88] Federal Republic of Germany (2001). *Web site for the Bundesbeauftragten für den Datenschutz.* Available online at: http://www.bfd.bund.de/

[89] Federal Republic of Germany (2001). *Links to the Landesbeauftragten für den Datenschutz* are available online at: http://www.datenschutz-berlin.de/sonstige/behoerde/ldbauf.htm

[90] Federal Republic of Germany (1996). *Telecommunications Carriers Data Protection Ordinance (TDSV)* of 12 July 1996 (Federal Law Gazette I p 982). Federal Ministry of Posts and Telecommunications. Available online at: http://www.datenschutz-berlin.de/gesetze/medien/tdsve.htm

[91] Federal Republic of Germany (1997). *Federal Act Establishing the General Conditions for Information and Communication Services. Information and Communication Services Act (Informations- und Kommunikationsdienste-Gesetz - IuKDG)* of 13 June 1997. Available online at: http://www.datenschutz-berlin.de/gesetze/medien/iukdge.htm

[92] Republic of Greece (1975). *Constitution of Greece*, adopted on 11 June 1975. Available online at: http://www.uni-wuerzburg.de/law/gr00t_.html

[93] Republic of Greece (1997). *Law no. 2472 on the Protection of Individuals with regard to the Processing of Personal Data.*

[94] Republic of Ireland (1937). *Constitution of Ireland*, enacted on 1st July 1937 and last amended on 23 June 1999 (Twentieth Amendment of the Constitution Act). Available on line at: http://www.irlgov.ie/taoiseach/publication/constitution/english/contents.htm

[95] Republic of Ireland (1998). *Data Protection Act 1998*. Available online at: http://elj.warwick.ac.uk/jilt/dp/1eire/eire1.htm

[96] Republic of Ireland (1996). *Consultation Paper on Privacy: Surveillance and the Interception of Communications*. The Law Reform Commission of Ireland

[97] Republic of Ireland (2001). *Web site of the Data Protection Commissioner*. Available online at: http://www.privacyexchange.org/legal/nat/omni/irelandsum.html

[98] Republic of Ireland (1997). *Freedom of Information Act, 1997*. Available online at: http://www.irlgov.ie/finance/free1.htm

[99] Republic of Italy (1947). *Constitution*. Adopted 22 Dec 1947. Available online at: http://www.uni-wuerzburg.de/law/it00t_.html

[100] Republic of Italy (1996). *Legge 31 dicembre 1996 no. 675, Tutela delle persone e di altri soggetti rispetto al trattamento dei dati personali*. Amended by Legislative Decree no. 123 of 9 May 1997 and 255 of 28 July 1997. Available online at: http://elj.strath.ac.uk/jilt/dp/material/l675-eng.htm

[101] Republic of Italy (1996). *Legge 31 dicembre 1996 no. 676, Delega al Governo in materia di tutela delle persone e di altri soggetti rispetto al trattamento dei dati personali*. Available online at: http://www.privacy.it/legge96676.html

[102] Grand Duchy of Luxembourg (1868). *Constitution of the Grand Duchy of Luxembourg*. Adopted on 17 October 1868 and last updated on 5 November 1998. Available online at: http://www.uni-wuerzburg.de/law/lu00t_.html

[103] Grand Duchy of Luxembourg (1979). *Act on the Use of Nominal Data in Computer Processing*. Adopted 31 March 1979

[104] Grand Duchy of Luxembourg (1999*). Projet de loi relatif au commerce électronique, document parlementaire N° 4554*. Adopted 12 July 2000. Available online at: http://rechtsinformatik.jura.uni-sb.de/cbl/cbl-journal0899.php

[105] Grand Duchy of Luxembourg (2000). *Projet de loi relatif au commerce électronique, document parlementaire No 4641*. Adopted by the Chambre des Deputes, Session ordinaire 1999-2000. Available online at: http://www.etat.lu/ECO/lois/index.htm

[106] Kingdom of the Netherlands (1989). *Constitution*. Available online at: http://www.uni-wuerzburg.de/law/nl00000_.html

[107] Kingdom of the Netherlands (2000). *Klant in het web*, June 2000. Available online at: http://www.registratiekamer.nl/bis/top_1_5_35_13.html

[108] Kingdom of the Netherlands (2000). *Personal Data Protection Act (Wet bescherming persoonsgegevens)*. Passed the Upper House of the Dutch Parliament, Session 1999-2000, Nr. 92, 25 892 - Rules for the protection of personal data on 3 July 2000 as a Revised Bill approved by the Lower House on 23 November 1999 , Staatsblad 2000 302, 6 July 2000. Available online at: http://home.planet.nl/~privacy1/ and http://www2.unimaas.nl/~privacy/wbp_en_rev.htm

[109]   Kingdom of the Netherlands (2001). Available online at:
         http://www.registratiekamer.nl

[110]   Kingdom of the Netherlands (1993). *Decree on Sensitive Data*, 5 March 1993.
         Available online at: http://www2.unimaas.nl/~privacy/bgg-e.htm

[111]   Kingdom of the Netherlands (1993). *Decree on Regulated Exemption*, 6 July
         1993. Available online at: http://www.unimaas.nl/~privacy/bgv.htm

[112]   Kingdom of the Netherlands (1998). *Telecommunications Act*. December 1998.
         Available online at: http://www.minvenw.nl/hdtp/hdtp2/wetsite/engels/index.html

[113]   Kingdom of the Netherlands (1997). *Dutch Medical Examinations Act 1997*.
         Available online at: http://www.unimaas.nl/~privacy/wmk.htm

[114]   Kingdom of the Netherlands (1997). *Dutch Medical Treatment Act 1997*. Available
         online at: http://www.unimaas.nl/~privacy/index.htm

[115]   Kingdom of the Netherlands (1997). *Compulsory Identification Act, Dutch Social
         Security System Act 1997*. Available online at:
         http://www.unimaas.nl/~privacy/osv1997.htm

[116]   Kingdom of the Netherlands (1991). *Government Information (Public Access) Act
         of 31 October 1991*

[117]   Republic of Portugal (1976). *Constitution*. Adopted on 2 April 1976. Available
         online at: http://www.uni-wuerzburg.de/law/po00000_.html

[118]   Republic of Portugal (1976). *Article 35 of the Constitution*. Available online at:
         http://www.cnpd.pt/Leis/leis.htm

[119]   Republic of Portugal (1998). *Lei da Protecção de Dados Pessoais, Lei nº 67/98*,
         26 October 1998. Available online at:
         http://www.websamba.com/derecho/anexos/anexonº200.htm

[120]   Republic of Portugal (1998). *Lei nº 69/98 de 28 de outubro de 1998 que regula o
         tratamento dos dados pessoais e a protecção da privacidade no sector das
         telecomunicações (transpõe a Directiva 97/66/EC, do Parlamento Europeu e do
         Conselho, de 15 de dezembro de 1997)*. Available online at:
         http://www.cnpd.pt/Leis/leis.htm

[121]   Republic of Portugal (2001). *Web site da Comissão Nacional de Protecção de
         Dados (National Data Protection Commission)*. Available online at:
         http://www.cnpd.pt/

[122]   Kingdom of Spain (1992). *Constitution of Spain*, amendment 27 August 1992.
         Available online at: http://www.uni-wuerzburg.de/law/sp00t_.html

[123]   Kingdom of Spain (1985). *Agreement on the Council of Europe Convention for the
         Protection of Individuals with Regard to the Automatic Processing of Personal
         Data, Strasbourg 28 January 1981*. Ratified by decision published in the Spanish
         Official Journal (BOE) of 15 November 1985

[124]   Kingdom of Spain (1992). *Ley Organica 5/1992 de 29 de Octubre de Regulación
         del Tratamiento Automatizado de los Datos de Caracter Personal (LORTAD). Ley
         Orgánica 15/99 de 13 de Diciembre de Protección de Datos de Carácter
         Personal*. Available online at: https://www.agenciaprotecciondatos.org/datd1.htm

[125]   Kingdom of Spain (1999). *Organic Law 15/1999, of 11 December on the Protection of Personal Data (LORPD) and Royal Decree RD 994/1999 of 11 June*

[126]   Kingdom of Spain (2001). *Web page of the Data protection Agency (Agencia de Protección de Datos).* Available online at: https://www.agenciaprotecciondatos.org

[127]   Kingdom of Spain (1992). *Ley 30/1992, de 26 de Noviembre, de Régimen Jurídico de las Administraciones Públicas y del Procedimiento Administrativo Común.* Available online at: http://www.um.es/siu/marco/30-92.htm

[128]   Kingdom of Spain (1986). *General Health Bill of 25 April 1986* (Articles 8, 10, 18, 23 and 61)

[129]   Kingdom of Spain (1994). *Law 11/1994 on Health Regulation of the Canary Islands*

[130]   Kingdom of Spain (1984). *Law 26/1984 of 19 July for the Protection of Consumers and Users*

[131]   Kingdom of Spain (1993). *Royal Decree RD 561/1993 of 16 April on Clinical Trials with Pharmaceuticals*

[132]   Kingdom of Spain (1995). *Royal Decree 63/1995, of 20 January on the Regulation of Health Care Services Provision of the National Health System.* Annex I, Ap.5

[133]   Kingdom of Spain (1989). *Law of the Public Statistics Function.* Law 12/1989 of 9 May

[134]   Kingdom of Spain (1996). *Royal Decree RD 208/1996 of 9 February About the Regulation of the Provision of Administrative Information Services to the Citizen*

[135]   Kingdom of Sweden (1974). *Regeringsformen, SFS 1974:152*

[136]   Kingdom of Sweden (1998). *The Personal Data Act (Personuppgiftslagen) SFS 1998:204.* Available online at: http://www.datainspektionen.se/in_english/legislation/data.shtml

[137]   Kingdom of Sweden (1973). *Data Act of 1973 (Datalagen) SFS 1973:289*

[138]   Kingdom of Sweden (2001). *Web site for the Data Inspection Board (Datainspektionen).* Available online at: http://www.din.se/

[139]   United Kingdom (1994). *Code of Practice on Access to Government Information of 4 April 1994, revised in January 1997.* Available online at: http://www.cfoi.org.uk/coptext.html

[140]   United Kingdom (1997). *Human Rights Bill, CM 3782, October 1997.* Available online at: http://www.official-documents.co.uk/document/hoffice/rights/rights.htm

[141]   United Kingdom (1998). *Data Protection Act 1998 (c.29).* Available online at: http://www.hmso.gov.uk/acts/acts1998/19980029.htm

[142]   United Kingdom (1984). *Data Protection Act 1984 (c.35).* Available online at: http://www.hmso.gov.uk/acts/acts1984/1984035.htm

[143]   United Kingdom (2001). *Web page of the Data Protection Commissioner,* formerly known as the Data Protection Registrar. Available online at: http://www.dataprotection.gov.uk/

[144] United Kingdom (1999). *Study of the Availability and Use of Personal Information in Public Registers*. Final Report to the Office of the Data Protection Registrar. Davies JE, Oppenheim C. Loughborough University, September 1999. Available online at: http://wood.ccta.gov.uk/dpr/dpdoc.nsf

[145] United Kingdom (1990). *Access to Medical Reports Act 1988 and the Access to Health Records Act 1990*

[146] United Kingdom (2000). *Regulation of Investigatory Powers Act 2000*. Available online at: http://www.homeoffice.gov.uk/ripa/ripact.htm

[147] United Kingdom National Health Services (2000). *Good Practices Guidelines for General Practice Electronic Patient Records Version 2.6*. The Joint Computing Group of the General Practitioners' Committee and the Royal College of General Practitioners. The NHS Executive General and Personal Medical Services Branch, Richmond House, London. Available online at: http://www.doh.gov.uk/gpepr/guidelines.pdf

[148] Republic of Bulgaria (1991). *Constitution of the Republic of Bulgaria* of 13 July 1991. Available online at: http://www.uni-wuerzburg.de/law/bu00t_.html

[149] Republic of Bulgaria (2000). *Access to Public Information Act*. Available online at: http://www.aip-bg.org/documents/access.htm

[150] Republic of Estonia (1991). *Constitution of Estonia*. Available online at: http://www.uni-wuerzburg.de/law/en00t_.html

[151] Republic of Estonia (1996). *Law on the Protection of Personal Data* (RT I 1996, 48, 944). Available online at: http://www.dp.gov.ee/eng/Personal_Data_Protection_Act.html

[152] Republic of Estonia (1997). *Databases Act* (RT I 1997, 28, 423) . Available online at: http://www.dp.gov.ee/eng/Databases_Act.html

[153] Republic of Estonia (2001). *Data Protection Inspectorate*. Web page at: http://www.dp.gov.ee:8020/

[154] Republic of Estonia (2000). *Digital Signatures Act* (RT I 2000, 26, 150) passed 8 March 2000, entered into force 15 December 2000. Available online at: http://www.riik.ee/riso/digiallkiri/digsignact.rtf

[155] Republic of Hungary (1949). *Constitution of the Republic of Hungary*. Last amended in 1997. Available online at: http://www.uni-wuerzburg.de/law/hu00000_.html

[156] Republic of Hungary (1991). *Constitutional Court Decision No. 15-AB of 13 April 1991*. Available online at: http://www.privacyinternational.org/countries/hungary/hungarian_id_decision_1991.html

[157] Republic of Hungary (1992). *Act on the Protection of Personal Data and the Publicity of Data of Public Interest (Act LXIII of 1992)*. Available online at: http://www.osa.ceu.hu/yeast/AccessAndProtection/04.htm

[158] Republic of Hungary (1999). *Act No. LXXII of 1999*

[159] Republic of Hungary (2001). *Parliamentary Commissioner for Data Protection and Freedom of Information*. Web site: http://www.obh.hu/

[160] Republic of Hungary (1992). *Act on the Register of Personal Data and Addresses of Citizens (Act No. LXVI of 1992)*

[161] Republic of Hungary (1996). *Act on the Identification Methods Replacing the Universal Personal Identification Number and on the Use of Identification Codes (Act No. XX of 1996)*

[162] Republic of Hungary (1997). *Act on the Use and Protection of Medical and Related Data (Act XLVII of 1997)*

[163] Republic of Hungary (1995). *Act on Public Records, Public Archives, and the Protection of Private Archives (Act No. LXVI of 1995)*

[164] Republic of Hungary (1992). *Act on Telecommunications (Act No. LXXII of 1992)*

[165] Republic of Hungary (1995). *Act on the Use of Name and Address Information Serving the Purposes of Research and Direct Marketing (Act No. CXIX of 1995)*

[166] Republic of Iceland (1944). *Constitution of Iceland* of 17 June 1944, as amended 30 May 1984 and 31 May 1991. Available online at: http://www.urich.edu/~jpjones/confinder/Iceland2.htm

[167] Republic of Iceland (2000). *Act on Protection of Individuals with Regard to the Processing of Personal Data No. 77/2000.* Available online at: http://brunnur.stjr.is/interpro/tolvunefnd/tolvunefnd.nsf/pages/1E685B166D04084 D002569050056BF6F

[168] Republic of Iceland (1989). *Act on the Registration and Handling of Personal Data, No. 121* of 28 December 1989.

[169] Republic of Iceland (1998). *Act on a Health Sector Database no. 139/1998* of 17 December 1998. Available online at: http://brunnur.stjr.is/interpro/htr/htr.nsf/pages/gagngr-log-ensk

[170] Republic of Iceland (2000). *Act on Biobanks no. 110/2000* of May 13, 2000. Available online at: http://brunnur.stjr.is/interpro/tolvunefnd/tolvunefnd.nsf/pages/95EAE39BAC9DFA 25002569050057034C

[171] Republic of Iceland (1996). *Act no. 50/1996.* Available online at: http://www.rz.uni-frankfurt.de/~sobotta/Enskthyd.doc

[172] Republic of Latvia (1991). *Constitutional Law on the Rights and Obligations of a Citizen and a Person.* Available online at: http://www.uni-wuerzburg.de/law/lg03000_.html

[173] Republic of Latvia (2001). *Regulatory Developments: Latvia Master Report.* Available online at: http://www.eu-esis.org/esis2reg/LVreg1.htm

[174] Republic of Latvia (1998). *Law on Freedom of Information*, adopted 29 October 1998 and signed 6 November 1998

[175] Republic of Lithuania (1992). *Constitution of the Republic of Lithuania* of 25 October 1992. Available online at: http://www.litlex.lt/Litlex/Eng/Frames/Laws/Documents/constitu.htm

[176] Republic of Lithuania (1996). *The Law on Legal Protection of Personal Data (No 63-1479, 1996).* Available online at: http://www.lrs.lt/cgi-bin/preps2?Condition1=38025&Condition2=

[177] Republic of Lithuania (1998). *Law No. VII-662* of 12 March 1998

[178] Republic of Lithuania (1996). *The Law on the Public Registers of 13 August 1996 (No. I-1490)*. Available online at: http://www.is.lt/dsinsp/anglo/docs/lst_reg.htm

[179] Republic of Lithuania (2000). *New Revision Law on Legal Protection of Personal Data of the Republic of Lithuania*. Available online at: http://www.is.lt/dsinsp/anglo/index.html

[180] Republic of Lithuania (1996). *Resolution No. 1185 establishing the State Data Protection Inspectorate of 10 October 1996 (No 100-2293)*

[181] Republic of Lithuania (2001). *Web page of the State Data Protection Inspectorate*: http://www.is.lt/dsinsp/anglo/index.html

[182] Republic of Lithuania (1995). *The Law on Telecommunications of 30 November 1995 (No. I-1109)*

[183] Republic of Lithuania (1993). *The Law on Statistics of 12 October 1993 (No. I-270)*

[184] Republic of Lithuania (1992). *Law on the Population Register of 23 January 1992 (No. I-2237)*

[185] Republic of Lithuania (1994). *Law on the Health System of 19 July 1994 (No. I-552)*

[186] Republic of Lithuania (1996). *The Law on the Provision of Information to the Public, 2 July 1996 No. I-1418*, amended in 23 January 1997. Available online at: http://www.lrtv.lt/en_lrtvm.htm

[187] Kingdom of Norway (1814). *Constitution of the Kingdom of Norway*. Available online at: http://odin.dep.no/ud/nornytt/uda-121.html

[188] Kingdom of Norway (2000). *Lov 2000-04-14 nr 31 Lov om behandling av personopplysninger (personopplysningsloven)*. Available online at: http://www.lovdata.no/all/hl-20000414-031.html

[189] Kingdom of Norway (1978). *Personal Data Registers Act of 1978 (Lov om personregistre mm av 9 juni 1978 nr 48)*. Available online at: http://www.datatilsynet.no/eksternweb/informasjon/engelsk/lov-eng.htm

[190] Kingdom of Norway (2001). *Data Inspectorate (Datatilsynet)*. Web site at: http://www.datatilsynet.no/

[191] Kingdom of Norway (1995). *The Telecommunications Act* of 23 June 1995.

[192] Kingdom of Norway (1970). *The Freedom of Information Act of 1970 (Lov om offentlighet i forvaltningen av 19 juni 1970 nr 69)*. Amended by Act No. 47 of 11 June 1982 and Act no. 86 of 17 December 1982 and Act of 10 January 1997 No. 7. Available online at: http://www.ub.uio.no/ujur/ulovdata/lov-19700619-069-eng.pdf

[193] Republic of Poland (1997). *The Constitutional Act of 1997*. Available online at: http://www.sejm.gov.pl/eng/konst/kon1.htm

[194] Republic of Poland (1997). *Law on Protection of Personal Data, Dz.U. nr 133, poz. 833* of 29 October 1997

[195]   Republic of Poland (2001). *Bureau of Inspector General for the Protection of Personal Data*. Web site at: http://www.giodo.gov.pl

[196]   Republic of Poland (1999). *The Classified Information Protection Act* of 22 January 1999

[197]   Russian Federation (1993). *Constitution of the Russian Federation*. Available online at: http://www.friends-partners.org/oldfriends/constitution/russian-const-ch2.html

[198]   Russian Federation (1995). *Russian Federation Federal Act No. 24-FZ, Law of the Russian Federation on Information, Informatization, and Information Protection of 25th January 1995*. Available online at: http://www.datenschutz-berlin.de/gesetze/internat/fen.htm

[199]   Russian Federation (1995). *Russian Federation Federal Act No. 15-FZ*. Adopted by the State Duma on 20 January 20 1995

[200]   Russian Federation (1994). *Civil Code, Article 19. RF Act No. 51-FZ*. Adopted by the State Duma on 21 October 1994

[201]   Russian Federation (1996). *The Criminal Code of the Russian Federation No. 63-FZ of 13 June 1996*

[202]   Slovak Republic (1992). *Constitution of the Slovak Republic*. Available online at: http://www.sanet.sk/Slovakia/Court/const.html

[203]   Slovak Republic (1998). *Act No. 52 on Protection of Personal Data in Information Systems*. Available online at: http://www.statistics.sk/webdata/english/acts/act5298/act5298.htm

[204]   Slovak Republic (1998). *Decree of the Statistical Office of the Slovak Republic of 11 May 1998*. Available online at: http://www.statistics.sk/webdata/english/acts/155decre/155decre.htm

[205]   Slovak Republic (1992). *Act on Protection of Personal Data in Information Systems (No. 256/92)*

[206]   Slovak Republic (2001). *Statistical Office of the Slovak Republic*. Web page at: http://www.statistics.sk/webdata/english/index2.htm

[207]   Slovak Republic (2000). *Act on Free Access to Information*. Available online at: http://www.infozakon.sk/zakon-schvalenyvnrsr.htm

[208]   Republic of Slovenia (1991). *Constitution of the Republic of Slovenia*. Available online at: http://www.sigov.si/us/eus-usta.html

[209]   Republic of Slovenia (1991). *Law on Personal Data Protection* . Uradni list Republike Slovenije (Official Journal of the Republic of Slovenia) No. 59/99, effective since 7 August 1999

[210]   Republic of Slovenia (1990). *Law on Personal Data Protection of 7 March 1990*. Published in the Uradni list Republike Slovenije No. 8/90, 38/90, 10/91, 19/91, 17/91, 13/93, 66/93

[211]   Republic of Slovenia (1995). *Law on National Statistics of 25 July 1995*. Amended in 2001; Uradni list Republike Slovenije No 9-529/2001. Available online at: http://www.sigov.si/zrs/eng/szaknov.doc

[212]   Republic of Slovenia (1997). *Law on Telecommunications*. Available online at: http://www.gov.si/urst/angl/docum/decr/a35_97.htm

[213]   Republic of Slovenia (2000). *The Electronic Commerce and Electronic Signature Act*. Available online at: http://www.gov.si/ep/ecaes.doc

[214]   Swiss Confederation (1874). *Constitution of Switzerland*. Available online at: http://www.uni-wuerzburg.de/law/sz01000_.html

[215]   Swiss Confederation (1999). *Constitution of Switzerland, 1999*. Available online at: http://www.uni-wuerzburg.de/law/sz00000_.html

[216]   Swiss Confederation (1992). *Loi fédérale sur la protection des données (LPD) du 19 juin 1992*. Available online at: http://www.admin.ch/ch/f/rs/235_1/index.html

[217]   European Union (1999). *Working Party on the Protection of Individuals with Regard to the Processing of Personal Data, Opinion 5/99 on the level of protection of personal data in Switzerland*, 7 June 1999. Available online at: http://europa.eu.int/comm/dg15/en/media/dataprot/wpdocs/wp22fr.pdf

[218]   Swiss Confederation (2001). *Federal Data Protection Commission*. Web site at: http://www.edsb.ch/

[219]   Swiss Confederation (1979). *Art 66-73, Procédure pénal fédérale. Loi de 23 Mars 1979 sur la protection de la vie priveé* and *Ordinance du 1er décembre 1997 sur le service de surveillance de la correspondance postale et des télécommunications*. Available online at: ttp://www.admin.ch/ch/f/rs/c780_11.html

[220]   Swiss Confederation (1907). *Section 28 of the Civil Code*, 10 December 1907

[221]   Swiss Confederation (1907). *Swiss Confederation Code pénal, Titre troisiéme: Infractions contre l'honneur et contre le domaine secret ou le domaine privé, Art 173-179*

[222]   Swiss Confederation (1997). *Telecommunications Law (LTC) of 30 April 1997*. Available online at: http://www.admin.ch/ch/f/rs/c784_10.html

[223]   Swiss Confederation (1997). *Office fédéral de la statistique, La protection des données dans la statistique médicale, 1997*. Available online at: http://www.admin.ch/bfs/stat_ch/ber14/statsant/ff1403c.htm

[224]   Swiss Confederation (1993). *Ordinance du 14 juin 1993 concernant les autorisations de lever le secret professionnel en matière de recherche médicale (OALSP), 14 juin 1993*. Available online at: http://www.admin.ch/ch/f/rs/c235_154.html

[225]   Swiss Confederation (1992). *Ordinance du 31 août 1992 sur le système provisoire de traitement des données relatives à la protection de l'Etat*. Available online at: http://www.admin.ch/ch/f/rs/c172_213_60.html

[226]   Swiss Confederation (1993). *Ordinance du 14 juin 1993 relative à la loi fédérale sur la protection des données (OLPD)*. Available online at: http://www.admin.ch/ch/f/rs/c235_11.html

[227]   Swiss Confederation (1995). *Ordinance du 19 juin 1995 sur le système de recherches informatisées de police (RIPOL)*. Available online at: http://www.admin.ch/ch/f/rs/c172_213_61.html

[228]   Swiss Confederation (1994). *Ordinance du 18 mai 1994 relative à la carte d'identité suisse*. Available online at: http://www.admin.ch/ch/f/rs/c143_3.html

[229]   Republic of Ukraine (1996). *Constitution of Ukraine.* Adopted at the Fifth Session
        of the Verkhovna Rada of Ukraine on 28 June 1996. Available online at:
        http://alpha.rada.kiev.ua/const/conengl.htm

[230]   Republic of Ukraine (1992). *Statute "On information" of 2 October 1992 (# 2657-
        XII)*

[231]   Republic of Ukraine (1997). *Verdict of the Constitutional Court of Ukraine
        Concerning the case of the official treatment of Articles 3, 23, 31, 47, 48 of the
        Law of Ukraine "On information" and Article 12 of the Law of Ukraine "On the
        Prosecutor's Office" October 30, 1997.* Available online at:
        http://www2.datatestlab.com/privacy/files/enclosure.doc

[232]   Pazyuk A (1999). *Privacy Ukraine: Privacy of Data Subject in Ukraine.* Available
        online at: http://www2.datatestlab.com/privacy/

[233]   Republic of Ukraine (1992). *Law of the 19th of September 1992*

[234]   Republic of Ukraine (1998). *Law "On prevention of AIDS contamination and social
        aid on civilians"* as well as *Article 13 of the Discipline of medical inspection on
        HIV results, registration of HIV and AIDS persons and medical care*, approved by
        the Statutory Order of the CM of 18 December 1998

[235]   Republic of Argentina (1994). *Constitution (Constitución de la Nación Argentina).*
        Available online at: http://www.constitution.org/cons/argentin.htm

[236]   Republic of Argentina (1998). *Ley de Protección de los Datos Personales* of 26
        November 1998 S.577/98, S.684/98, S.1582/98, S.1094/98, S. 277/98. Available
        online at: http://www.derechos.org/nizkor/arg/ley/data.html

[237]   Republic of Argentina (1994). *Código Procesual Penal de la Nación, Art. 236*

[238]   Palazzi PA (1999). *El derecho de acceso a la información pública en la ley N°
        104 de la Ciudad Autónoma de Buenos Aires.* REDI Número 11; Junio de 1999.
        Available online at:
        http://publicaciones.derecho.org/redi/index.cgi?/N%FAmero_11_-_Junio_de_1999

[239]   Federative Republic of Brazil (1988). *Constitution of Brazil* (Constituição da
        República Federativa do Brasil). Available online at:
        http://www.uni-wuerzburg.de/law/br00t_.html

[240]   Federative Republic of Brazil (1984). *Law No. 7.232 of 29 October 1984*

[241]   Federative Republic of Brazil (1990). *Law No. 8.078 of 11September 1990*

[242]   Federative Republic of Brazil (1988). *Federal Senate Bill No. 61/1996.* Available
        online at: http://www.privacyexchange.org/legal/ppl/nat/brazilpending.html

[243]   Stammer L (2000). *Brazil and its neighbors; realizing the possibilities.* Healthcare
        Informatics, August: 26-37. McGraw-Hill; Minneapolis MN. Available online at:
        http://www.healthcare-informatics.com/issues/2000/08_00/cover.htm

[244]   Canada (1982). *Canadian Charter of Rights and Freedoms.* Available online at:
        http://canada.justice.gc.ca/Loireg/charte/const_en.html

[245]   Canada (2000). *Charting Our Future Together: Consultation On A Draft Charter
        Of Privacy Rights by The Hon. Sheila Finestone, P.C. of 9 March 2000.* Available
        online at: http://www.ltinc.net/fipa/finestone1.htm

[246]   Canada (2000). *Personal Information Protection and Electronic Documents Act, 48-49 Elizabeth II, Chapter 5*. 36th Parliament of Canada, House Government Bills (Bill C-6). Available on line at: http://www.parl.gc.ca/36/2/parlbus/chambus/house/bills/government/C-6/C-6_4/90052bE.html

[247]   Canada (1985). *Privacy Act (R.S. 1985, c. P-21)*. Available online at: http://canada.justice.gc.ca/stable/EN/Laws/Chap/P/P-21.html

[248]   Canada (2001). *Privacy Commissioner of Canada*. Web site at: http://www.privcom.gc.ca

[249]   Canada (2000). *Privacy: Provincial Laws and Commissions*. A list of state laws and commissions is available online at: http://infoweb.magi.com/~privcan/other.html

[250]   Canada (2000). *Charter of Rights of the Province of Quebec*. Available online at: http://www.cai.gouv.qc.ca/commiss.htm

[251]   Canada (2000). *The Electronic Commerce Act of the Province of Ontario, Bill 88-2000. An Act to promote the use of information technology in commercial and other transactions by resolving legal uncertainties and removing statutory barriers that affect electronic communication. 37th Legislature, Legislative Assembly of Ontario*. Available online at: http://www.ontla.on.ca/library/bills/88371.htm

[252]   Canada (1999). *Report of the Standing Committee on Human Resources Development and the Status of Persons with Disabilities, "Beyond the Numbers: The Future of the Social Insurance Number System in Canada," May 1999*. Available online at: http://www.parl.gc.ca/InfocomDoc/36/1/HRPD/Studies/Reports/hrpdrp04-e.htm#TOC

[253]   Canada (1985). *Access to Information Act (R.S. 1985, c. A-1)*. Available on line at: http://canada.justice.gc.ca/STABLE/EN/Laws/Chap/A/A-1.html

[254]   Canada (2001). *Information Commissioner of Canada*. Available online at: http://magi.com/~accessca/

[255]   COACH (Canada's Health Informatics Association) (2001). *Guidelines for the Protection of Health Information*. Toronto, ON; ISBN 0-9688851 0 1

[256]   Republic of Chile (1980). *Constitution of Chile*. Available online at: http://www.georgetown.edu/LatAmerPolitical/Constitutions/Chile/chile97.html

[257]   Republic of Chile (1999). *Law for the Protection of Private Life (Ley Sobre Protección de la Vida Privada), Law No.19628 of 30 August 1999*

[258]   Republic of Colombia (1999). *Ley 527 de agosto 18 de 1999*. Available online at: http://www.sic.gov.co/Normatividad/Leyes/Ley%20527-99.htm

[259]   Republic of Colombia (2000). *Decreto Número 1747 de 2000*. Passed by the Presidency on 11 September 2000. Available online at: http://www.interfaz.com/comercioelectronico/decreto 1747.html

[260]   United Mexican States (1917). *Constitution (Constitución Política de los Estados Unidos Mexicanos)*. Available online at: http://www.juridicas.unam.mx/infjur/leg/

[261]   United Mexican States (2000). *E-Commerce Act*. Available online at: http://www.bmck.com/ecommerce/mexico-memo.doc

[262]   Republic of Peru (1993). *Constitution of Peru*. Available online at:
         http://www.asesor.com.pe/teleley/5000%2Din.htm

[263]   Republic of Peru (1999). *Proyecto No. 5233, Ley Sobre la Privacidad de los
         Datos Informaticos y la Creacion del Comisionado para la Proteccion de la
         Privacidad*

[264]   Republic of Peru (1995). *Ley Organica del Registro Nacional de Identificacion y
         Estado Civil, Ley No. 26497* of 11 July 1995. Available online at:
         http://www.congreso.gob.pe/ccd/leyes/cronos/1995/ley26497.htm

[265]   Republic of Peru (1995). *Ley de aplicación de la acción constitucional del habeas
         data, Ley No. 26301* of 13 November 1995. Available online at:
         http://www.asesor.com.pe/teleley/bull505.htm

[266]   United States of America (1967). *Katz v. U.S., 386 U.S. 954 (1967)*. Available
         online at: http://laws.findlaw.com/US/386/954.html

[267]   United States of America (1995). *McIntire v. Ohio Elections Committee, 19 April
         1995*

[268]   United States of America (1958). *NAACP v. Alabama, 357 U.S. 449 (1958)*.
         Available online at: http://laws.findlaw.com/US/357/449.html

[269]   United States of America (2000). *Reno v. Condon, No. 98-1464, 12 January
         2000*. Available online at: http://supct.law.cornell.edu/supct/html/98-1464.ZS.html

[270]   United States of America (1974). *Privacy Act of 1974, 5 USC 552a, PL 93-579*.
         Available online at: http://www.epic.org/privacy/laws/privacy_act.html

[271]   United States of America (2000). *FTC Privacy Pages*. Available online at:
         http://www.ftc.gov/privacy/index.html

[272]   United States of America (2000). *Privacy Online: Fair Information Practices in the
         Electronic Marketplace: A Federal Trade Commission Report to Congress (May
         2000)*. Available online at: http://www.ftc.gov/os/2000/05/index.htm#22

[273]   Smith RE (1997). *Compilation of State and Federal Privacy Laws by Robert Ellis
         Smith and Privacy Journal*. Available online at:
         http://www.epic.org/privacy/consumer/states.html

[274]   United States of America (1996). *Freedom of Information Act, 5 USC 552, 1966*.
         Available online at: http://www.epic.org/open_gov/foia/us_foia_act.html

[275]   United States of America (1996). *Electronic Freedom of Information Act
         Amendments of 1996*. Available online at: http://www.epic.org/open_gov/efoia.htm

[276]   United States of America (1998). *Children's Online Privacy Protection Act of 1998
         (COPPA)*. Effective April 2000. Available online at:
         http://www.ftc.gov/opa/1999/9910/childfinal.htm

[277]   U.S. Department of Health and Human Services (2000). *Standards for Privacy of
         Individually Identifiable Health Information; Final Rule. Office of the Secretary 45
         CFR Parts 160 and 164 RIN: 0991–AB08*. Federal Register / Vol. 65, No. 250 /
         Thursday, December 28, 2000 / Rules and Regulations; Washington DC.
         Available online at: http://www.aspe.hhs.gov/admnsimp/bannerps.htm

[278]   Schoenberg R, Safran C (2000). *Internet based repository of medical records that
         retains patient confidentiality*. Br Med J 321(7270):1199-1203

[279]   Mandl KD, Szolovits P, Kohane IS (2001). *Public standards and patients' control: how to keep electronic medical records accessible but private.* Br Med J 322 (7281):283-287

[280]   U.S. Department of Health and Human Services (1998). *Security and Electronic Signature Standards; Proposed Rule. Office of the Secretary 45 CFR Part 142 [HCFA-0049-P] RIN: 0938-AI57.* Federal Register: August 12, 1998 (Volume 63, Number 155). Washington DC

[281]   DeMuro PR, Gantt WR 3rd (2001). *HIPAA privacy standards raise complex implementation issues.* Healthcare Financ Manag 55(1): 42-47

[282]   Health Privacy Project (2001). *Best Principles for Health Policy, a Report of the Health Privacy Working Group.* Institute for Health Care Research and Policy, Georgetown University. Washington, DC. Available online at: http://www.healthprivacy.org

[283]   European Parliament (2001). *Doubts over Security of Personal Data in U.S. "Safe Harbors".* Rapporteur: Paciotti O, Safe harbour privacy principles; Doc.: A5-0177/2000. Available online at: http://www.europarl.eu.int/dg3/sdp/brief/en/br000703_ens.htm#9

[284]   State of Israel (1994). *The Basic Law: Human Dignity and Freedom (5752-1992).* Passed by the Knesset on the 21st Adar, 5754 on 9 March 1994). Available online at: http://www.israel-mfa.gov.il/gov/laws/dignity.html

[285]   State of Israel (1985). *The Protection of Privacy Law 5741-1981, 1011 Laws of the State of Israel 128* as amended by the Protection of Privacy Law *(Amendment) 5745-1985*

[286]   State of Israel (1995). *The Computer Law (5755-1995), 1534 Laws of the State of Israel 366*

[287]   State of Israel (1996). *Patient's Rights Law, 5756-1996*

[288]   State of Israel (1990). *H.C. 1601-4/90 Shalit et al. v. Peres el at., 44(3) P.D. 353*

[289]   Republic of South Africa (1993). *The Interim Constitution* (Act 200 of 1993)

[290]   Republic of South Africa (2000). *Promotion of Access to Information Act No 2 of 2000.* Available online at: http://www.polity.org.za/govdocs/legislation/2000/index.html

[291]   Republic of Turkey (1982). *Constitution of the Republic of Turkey.* Available online at: http://www.mfa.gov.tr/GRUPI/Anayasa/i142.htm

[292]   Republic of Turkey (1998). *Turkish Republic Foreign Trade Office, E-Commerce Laws Working Party Report, 8 May 1998.* Available online at: http://kurul.ubak.gov.tr/e-ticaret.html

[293]   Commonwealth of Australia (1988). *An Act to Make Provision to Protect the Privacy of Individuals, and for Related Purposes (Privacy Act 1988).* Available online at: http://www.austlii.edu.au/au/legis/cth/consol_act/pa1988108/

[294]   Commonwealth of Australia (2000*). Privacy Amendment (Private Sector) Act 2000.* Available online at: http://www.privacy.gov.au/act/index.html

[295]   Commonwealth of Australia (2000). *Office of Privacy Commissioner.* Website available at: http://www.privacy.gov.au/

211

[296] Commonwealth of Australia (1979). *The Telecommunications (Interception) Act of 1979*. Available online at: http://www.austlii.edu.au/au/legis/cth/consol_act/ta1979350/

[297] Commonwealth of Australia (1997). *Telecommunications Act*. Available online at: http://www.austlii.edu.au/au/legis/cth/consol_act/dpata1990349/

[298] Commonwealth of Australia (1914). *The Crimes Act*. Available online at: http://www.austlii.edu.au/au/legis/cth/consol_act/ca191482/s85zl.html

[299] Commonwealth of Australia (1982). *Freedom of Information Act*. Available online at: http://www.austlii.edu.au/au/legis/cth/consol_act/foia1982222/

[300] People's Republic of China (1993). *Constitution*. Adopted at the Fifth Session of the Fifth National People's Congress. Available online at: http://www.qis.net/chinalaw/prccon5.htm

[301] People's Republic of China (1997). *Computer Information Network and Internet Security, Protection and Management Regulations*. Approved by the State Council on December 11, 1997 and promulgated by the Ministry of Public Security on December 30, 1997. Available online at: http://www.usembassy-china.gov/english/sandt/index.html

[302] People's Republic of China (1994). *Hong Kong Law Reform Commission, 1994 Report on the Law Relating to the Protection of Personal Data*. Available online at the Web site of the Hong Kong Law Reform Commission: http://www.info.gov.hk

[303] People's Republic of China (1995). *Hong Kong Code on Access to Information, March 1995*. Available online at: http://www.info.gov.hk/access/code.htm

[304] Republic of India (1949). *Constitution*. Available online at: http://www.commercenetindia.com/constitution/

[305] Republic of India (1998). *National Task Force on Information Technology and Software Development, Basic Background Report, 9th June 1998*. Available online at: http://it-taskforce.nic.in/it-taskforce/bg.htm

[306] Republic of India (2000). *Information Technology Act 2000, No. 21 of 2000*. Available online at: http://www.mit.gov.in/it-bill.htm

[307] Republic of India (2000). *Freedom on Information Bill*. Available online at: http://www.humanrightsinitiative.org/RTI/foibill1.htm

[308] Japan (1946). *Constitution*. Available online at: http://www.uni-wuerzburg.de/law/ja00000_.html

[309] Japan (1988).*The Act for the Protection of Computer Processed Personal Data held by Administrative Organs, Act No. 95, 16 December 1988* (Kampoo, 16 December 1988)

[310] Japan (1997). *Electronic Network Consortium Guideline for Protecting Personal Data in Electronic Network Management (Revised)*. Available online at: http://www.nmda.or.jp/enc/privacy-rev-english.html

[311] Japan (2000). *Advisory Panel to Japanese Government Drafts Law to Protect Personal Information*. BNA Daily Report for Executives, June 8, 2000.

[312]   Japan (1999). *The Law Concerning Access to Information Held by Administrative Organs.* Available online at:
http://www.somucho.go.jp/gyoukan/kanri/translation.htm

[313]   Republic of Korea (1948). *Constitution of the Republic of Korea.* Available online at: http://www.ccourt.go.kr/english/et.html

[314]   Republic of Korea (1994). *Act on the Protection of Personal Information Managed by Public Agencies of 7 January 1994*

[315]   Republic of Korea (1999). *Basic Law on Electronic Commerce.* Available online at: http://www.mbc.com/ecommerce/legis/south_korea.html

[316]   Republic of Korea (2000). *Ministry of Information and Communication Cyber Privacy Center.* Website available at: http://www.cyberprivacy.or.kr/

[317]   Republic of Korea (1997). *Electronic National Identification Card Project.* Available online at: http://kpd.sing-kr.org/idcard/main-e.html

[318]   Malaysia (1957). *Constitution.* Available online at:
http://www.uni-wuerzburg.de/law/my_indx.html

[319]   Malaysia (1998). *Communications and Multimedia Act 1998.* Available online at:
http://www.cmc.gov.my/legisframe.htm

[320]   Malaysia (1997). *Digital Signature Bill 1997.* Available online at:
http://www.cca.gov.my/1997.htm

[321]   Malaysia (1998*). Digital Signature Regulations 1998.* Available online at:
http://www.cca.gov.my/1998.htm

[322]   Malaysia (1997). *Computer Crimes Bill 1997.* Available online at:
http://www.mycert.mimos.my/crime.html

[323]   New Zealand (1993). *The Privacy Act 1993.* Available online at:
http://www.knowledge-basket.co.nz/privacy/legislation/1993028/toc.html

[324]   New Zealand (1993). *The Privacy Amendment Act 1993.* Available online at:
http://www.knowledge-basket.co.nz/privacy/legislation/1993059/toc.html

[325]   New Zealand (1994). *The Privacy Amendment Act 1994.* Available online at:
http://www.knowledge-basket.co.nz/privacy/legislation/1994070/toc.html

[326]   New Zealand (1996). *Privacy Amendment Act 1996.* Available online at:
http://rangi.knowledge-basket.co.nz/gpacts/public/text/1996/an/142.html

[327]   New Zealand (1997). *Privacy Amendment Act 1997.* Available online at:
http://rangi.knowledge-basket.co.nz/gpacts/public/text/1997/an/071.html

[328]   New Zealand (1998). *Privacy Amendment Act 1998.* Available online at:
http://rangi.knowledge-basket.co.nz/gpacts/public/text/1998/an/057.html

[329]   New Zealand (2000). *Privacy Amendment Act 2000.* Available online at:
http://rangi.knowledge-basket.co.nz/gpacts/public/text/2000/an/076.html

[330]   New Zealand (1991). *Privacy Commissioner Act 1991.* Available online at:
http://rangi.knowledge-basket.co.nz/gpacts/public/text/1991/an/126.html

[331]   New Zealand (1982). *Official Information Act 1982.* Available online at:
http://www.ombudsmen.govt.nz/official.htm

[332]   New Zealand (1987). *Local Government Official Information and Meetings Act 1987.* Available online at: http://www.ombudsmen.govt.nz/local.htm

[333]   New Zealand (2000). *Office of the Ombudsman.* Web page available at: http://www.ombudsmen.govt.nz/

[334]   Republic of the Philippines (1987). *Constitution.* Available online at: http://pdx.rpnet.com/consti/index.htm

[335]   Republic of the Philippines (1972). *Cordero v. Buigasco, 34130-R, April 17, 1972, 17 CAR (2s) 539*

[336]   Republic of the Philippines (1983). *Jaworski v. Jadwani, CV-66405, December 15, 1983*

[337]   Republic of the Philippines (2000). *Electronic Commerce Act, Republic Act No 8972.* Available online at: http://www.bknet.org/laws/ecomm.html

[338]   Republic of the Philippines (1987). *Republic Act 6713 of 1987.* Available online at: http://www.bknet.org/laws/ra6713.html

[339]   Republic of Singapore (1963). *Constitution.* Available online at: http://www.uni-wuerzburg.de/law/sn00t_.html

[340]   Tremewan C (1994). *The Political Economy of Social Control in Singapore.* St. Martin's Press

[341]   Republic of Singapore (1998). *Report of the National Internet Advisory Board 1997/1998, September 1998.* Available online at: http://www.sba.gov.sg/work/sba/internet.nsf/

[342]   Republic of Singapore (1998). *Computer Misuse Act (Chapter 50A).* Available online at: http://www.lawnet.com.sg/freeaccess/CMA.htm

[343]   Republic of Singapore (1998). *Electronic Transactions Act (Act 25 of 1998).* Available online at: http://www.lawnet.com.sg/freeaccess/ETA.htm

[344]   Republic of China (1946). *Constitution of the Republic of China.* Available online at: http://www.oop.gov.tw/roc/charter/echarter.htm

[345]   Republic of China (1995). *Computer-Processed Personal Data Protection Law of 11 August 1995.* Available online at: http://virtualtaiwan.com/members/guide/legal/cpdpl.htm

[346]   Republic of China (1995). *Computer-Processed Personal Data Protection Law Enforcement rules, 1 May 1996.* Available online at: http://virtualtaiwan.com/members/guide/legal/cpdpl2.htm

[347]   Republic of China (1996). *Telecommunications Law 1996, 5 February 1996.* Available online at: http://virtualtaiwan.com/members/guide/legal/telecom_law.html

[348]   Kingdom of Thailand (1997). *Constitution.* Available online at: http://www.krisdika.go.th/law/text/lawpub/e11102540/text.htm

[349]   Kingdom of Thailand (1997). *Official Information Act, B.E. 2540 (1997).* Available online at: http://www.krisdika.go.th/law/text/lawpub/e02092540/text.htm

[350] Kingdom of Thailand (2000). *Official Information Commission*. Website available at: http://www.oic.thaigov.go.th/

[351] Wellbery BS, Wolfe CC (1997). *Privacy in the Information Age*. Office of Service Industries, U.S. Department of Commerce, Washington DC. Available online at: http://www.ecommerce.gov/15.htm

[352] de Graaf G (2001). *European Data Privacy: 21st Century Challenges of Transatlantic Policy Cooperation in Electronic Commerce*. In Transatlantic Regulatory Harmonization and Global Standards, The George Washington University School of Business and Public Management, Washington DC, Januray 2001

[353] U.S. Federal Trade Commission (2000). *Joint Workshop on Alternative Dispute Resolution for Online Consumer Transactions*. U.S. Department of Commerce and Federal Trade Commission, June 6-7, 2000, Washington DC. Available online at: http://www.ftc.gov/bcp/altdisresolution

[354] U.S. Department of Commerce (2000). *Leadership for the New Millennium: Delivering On Digital Progress and Prosperity*. Working Group on Electronic Commerce Third Annual Report. Available online at: http://www.ecommerce.gov/ecomnews/ecommerce2000annual.pdf

[355] Better Business Bureau's Online Division (2001). *Code of Online Business Practices*. Available online at: http://www.bbbonline.com/code/code.asp

[356] Electronic Commerce Consumer Protection Group (2000). *Guidelines for Merchant-to-Consumer Transactions and Commentary*. Available online at: http://www.ecommercegroup.org/guidelines.htm

[357] U.S. Federal Trade Commission (2001). *Federal Trade Commission*. Website available at: http://www.ftc.gov

[358] Organization for Economic Cooperation and Development (2000). *Building Trust in the Online Environment: Business-to-Consumer Dispute Resolution*. Conference jointly organized by the Organization for Economic Cooperation and Development (OECD), Hague Conference on Private International Law (HCPIL), and International Chamber of Commerce (ICC). 11-12 December 2000, The Hague, The Netherlands. Available online at: http://www.oecd.org//dsti/sti/it/secur/act/Online_trust/biographies.htm

[359] U.S. Department of Commerce (2000). *Transcript of the Online Privacy Technologies Workshop and Technology Fair*. Washington, DC; 19 September 2000. Available online at: http://www.ntia.doc.gov/ntiahome/privacy/files/2000transcript.txt

[360] National Work Group on Literacy and Health (1998). *Communicating with patients who have limited literacy skills: report of the National Work Group on Literacy and Health*. J Fam Pract 46:168-175

[361] Internet Healthcare Coalition (2001). *IHC Website*. Available online at: http://www.ihealthcoalition.org/

[362] U.S. Federal Trade Commission (2001). *Federal Trade Commission Consumer and Business Publications on E-Commerce and the Internet*. Website available at: http://www.ftc.gov/bcp/menu-internet.htm

[363]   Sosa-Iudicissa M, Oliveri N, Gamboa CA, Roberts J (Editors) (1997). *Internet, Telematics and Health*. Studies in Health Technology and Informatics Volume 36. PAHO/WHO and International Medical Informatics Association. IOS Press, ISBN 90 5199 289 0

[364]   U.S. Government, The White House (2000). *Defending America's Cyberspace National Plan for Information Systems Protection: An Invitation to a Dialogue*. Available online at: http://www.ntia.doc.gov/osmhome/cip/national_plan_final.pdf

[365]   World Trade Organization (2000). *Legal Texts: the WTO Agreements of the Final Act of the 1986–1994 Uruguay Round of Trade Negotiations, Article XIV General Exceptions*. Available online at: http://www.wto.org/english/docs_e/legal_e/final_e.htm

[366]   U.S. Department of Commerce (2000). *Safe Harbor Workbook*. Available online at: http://www.export.gov/safeharbor/sh_workbook.html

[367]   U.S. Department of Commerce (2000). *Leadership for the New Millennium: Delivering on Digital Progress and Prosperity*. The U.S. Government Working Group on Electronic Commerce, Third Annual Report, Washington D.C. Available online at: http://www.ecommerce.gov/ecomnews/ecommerce2000annual.pdf

[368]   Alcántara CH (2001). *The Development Divide in a Digital Age: An Issues Paper*. United Nations Research Institute for Social Development, Technology, Business and Society Programme Paper Number 4, August; Geneva. ISSN 1020 8216. Available online at: ftp://ftp.unicc.org/unrisd/outgoing/pp/tbs/hewitt.pdf

[369]   Digital Opportunity Task Force (2001). *Digital opportunities for all: Meeting the Challenge*. Report of the DOT Force 11 May 2001. Available online at: http://www.dotforce.org/reports/DOT_Force_Report_V_5.0h.pdf

[370]   Eysenbach G (2001). *What is e-Health?*. J Med Internet Research 3(1):e20. Available online at: http://www.jmir.org/2001/2/e20/index.htm

[371]   Della Mea V (2001). *What is e-Health (2): The Death of Telemedicine?*. J Med Internet Research 3(2):e22. Available online at: http://www.jmir.org/2001/2/e22/index.htm

[372]   Digital Opportunity Task Force (2001). *Okinawa Charter on Global Information Society*. Official Documents of the Kyushu-Okinawa DOT Force Summit Meeting. Available online at: http://www.dotforce.org/reports/it1.html

[373]   Correa CM (2000). *Intellectual property Rights, the WLO and Developing Countries: The TRIPS Agreement and Policy Options*. Zed Books Ltd, London. ISBN 1-85649 737 2

[374]   ECOSOC (2000). *Development and International Cooperation in the Twenty-First Century: the Role of Information Technology in the Context of a Knowledge-Based Global Economy*. Draft ministerial declaration of the high-level segment submitted by the President of the United Nations Economic and Social Council, 11 July. Document ECOSOC E/2000/L.9. Available online at: http://www.un.org/esa/coordination/ecosoc/itforum/eclac.pdf

[375]   ECOSOC (2001). *Information and Communications (ICT) Taskforce: Report of the Secretary- General 20 February*. Document ECOSOC E/2001/7. Available online at: http://www.un.org/documents/ecosoc/docs/2001/e2001-7.pdf

[376]   ECLAC (2000). *Declaration of Florianópolis*. Regional Meeting on Information
         Technology for Development convened by the Government of the Federal
         Republic of Brazil and the United Nations Economic Commission for Latin
         America and the Caribbean; Florianópolis, SC, June 20-21. Available online at:
         http://www.eclac.cl/publicaciones/secretariaejecutiva/3/lcl1383/florianopoliseng.ht
         m

[377]   Federal Republic of Brazil (2000). *The Brasília Communiqué*. Declaration of the
         Heads of State at the Meeting of the Presidents of South America of August 31- 1
         September in Brasília. Available online at:
         http://www.brasilemb.org/policy/summit2000/communique.htm

[378]   Republic of Indonesia (2001). *Jakarta Declaration on Information and
         Communication Technology for Development*. Heads of State and Government of
         the Group of Fifteen Meeting in Jakarta, Indonesia, 30-31 May. Available online t:
         http://www.dfa-deplu.go.id/world/multilateral/g15/jkt-declaration2.htm

[379]   Federal Republic of Brazil (2001). *ICT for Development: the View of Developing
         Countries*. Declaration of the Representatives of twenty-eight developing
         countries of Africa, the Middle East, Asia, Oceania, Latin America and the
         Caribbean at the Intergovernmental Meeting on Information and Communication
         Technologies for Development, Rio de Janeiro, Brazil, 18-19 June. Available
         online at: http://www.socinfo.org.br/documentos/ict/rj_dec.htm

[380]   Republic of Chile (2001). *Declaration of Santiago*. Declaration of the Heads of
         State and Government of the Rio Grupo, Santiago, Chile, 17-18 August. Available
         online at: http://www.minrel.cl/grupoderio/Declaración-Santiago-Inglés.htm

[381]   Republic of Chile (2001). *Declaration of Santiago*. Declaration of the Rio Group
         and the European Union Tenth Minister's Meeting, Santiago, Chile, 28 March.
         Available online at: http://www.minrel.cl/grupoderio/10GRIO-UE.htm

[382]   ECOSOC (2001). *The Role of the United Nations in Promoting Development,
         Particularly with respect to Access to and Transfer of Knowledge and
         Technology, Especially Information and Communication technologies, Inter Alia
         Through Partnerships with Relevant Stakeholders, Including the Private Sector:
         Draft Agreed Conclusions Submitted by the Vice-President of the Council, 5 July*.
         Document ECOSOC E/2001/L.16. Available online at:
         http://www.un.org/documents/ecosoc/docs/2001/e2001-l16.pdf

217